THE MAGIC ANATOMY BOOK

The Magic Anatomy Book

Written and Illustrated by

Carol Donner

W. H. FREEMAN AND COMPANY

NEW YORK

Library of Congress Cataloging-in-Publication Data

Donner, Carol.
    The magic anatomy book.

    Summary: Relates the adventures of two children as
they journey through the human body and learn about its
structure.
    1. Anatomy, Human—Juvenile literature.   [1. Anatomy,
Human]   I. Title.
QM27.D66   1986   611   86-1073
ISBN 0-7167-1715-8

Printed in the United States of America
1 2 3 4 5 6 7 8 9 0   KP   4 3 2 1 0 8 9 8 7 6

To Robb

CHAPTER ONE

Max and Molly usually marched everywhere they went, mostly out of step, the same but reverse, opposite equals, as twins often are. Today they marched faster than usual, casting occasional glances up at the darkening, lowering sky. They left the road and started up the long hill to their grandmother's, hoping to beat the rain.

"We're not going to make it," said Molly, holding out her hand. "I felt a drop."

"Yes, we are. We're almost there," said Max, looking ahead at the stark, weathered house above them on the hill. Its many gables pointed up at the stone-gray sky of the gathering storm. Chill gusts of wind snatched loose leaves to dance with in tiny mad whirlwinds, dervishes celebrating the end of fall. The scene would have looked forbidding on this gloomy day except for two bright spots. A warm light glowed in the kitchen window of the old house, and an odd marmalade cat poked about outside, stalking the little creatures that lived in the weeds.

Max stuffed his hands farther down into his pockets and studied the sky. "A typical November storm," he observed. "Coming from the east, and that can mean bad weather this time of year. Cold air is colliding with warm"—

"Good grief, Max, you don't have to explain it all! Why can't you just say it's going to rain, like a normal person?" Molly sighed and kicked at some leaves.

"Because it's important to understand how things work. How else can you know what's going to happen?"

"Just look!" Molly waved at the sky. "Anybody can see it's going to rain . . . and we're going to be stuck inside for a whole Saturday afternoon. All your analyzing can't change that."

"I wasn't trying to change it, that's your department. Trot out your fairy godmother and make the sun shine."

"Oh, stop!" Molly laughed. They were at it again—a perpetual argument, taking opposite sides, neither giving an inch, never a victory, their private twin-hobby.

"Come on," Max challenged. "Let's beat the rain. I'll race you."

"Go!" Slickers flying, they dashed up the hill like yellow demons. Baxter, the marmalade cat, pricked up his ears and wiped his whiskers when he heard their voices. Just then, a huge raindrop plopped on his nose. Startled, he abandoned his adventures and headed for the house with the accelerating trot of a cat determined to stay dry. Too late. Lightning ripped open the sky and rain began to pour. With no time to reach the porch, he scrambled up onto a window ledge, puffed out his fur, and sat scowling at the raindrops that pursued his tail from the dripping eaves. Then, recognizing the yellow spots racing up the hill, he meowed and hopped down for one last dash to meet the twins on the porch.

"Beat you!" panted Max.

"Well, I was right. We didn't make it." Molly stomped to shake the water off her boots, giving the wet cat another shower.

"Grandma, we're here!" called Max, and stooped to pat Baxter. "Oh, boy, you're wet!" Baxter shook as hard as he could, and when the door opened, he shot through to his pillow to lick himself dry.

"Hang up your wet things," Grandma said. "Lunch is ready."

Molly eagerly sniffed the air. "There's something good in the oven. When can we eat it?"

"Not now, Molly, it would spoil your lunch."

"Shucks!"

"If Molly had her way, she'd live on candy bars," Max remarked.

"And you'd live on soda pop," Molly retorted.

"You'd both live on germs if I didn't have my way. Just look at those hands!" And she marched them off to wash. Molly muttered that she thought grandmothers were supposed to spoil you, and Max announced that less than 70 percent of germs are removed by the washing of hands. Then they sat down to soup and salad. Baxter licked his fur in a frenzy, first one spot then another, then back again, trying to dry it all at once. Finally satisfied, he hopped up on the empty kitchen chair to peep hopefully at their plates.

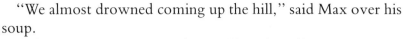

"We almost drowned coming up the hill," said Max over his soup.

"The rain was coming sideways!" said Molly.

Max looked up at their white-haired, somewhat frail grandmother and asked, "Aren't you scared sometimes up here?"

She shook her head. "No, and I wasn't even when I was little. The wind would howl down the chimney and shake the shutters, but I always felt safe. This old house and I are friends."

Molly stopped eating. "Is that why you don't want to move into town like everyone says you should?" She knew many people considered her grandmother as eccentric as her house.

"Do you think I should move?" asked Grandma.

"Not us!" Max hurried to reply. "Not if you don't want to.

We love to come here. I was just wondering if it isn't scary sometimes. And you're all alone."

Grandma's eyes twinkled. "Who said I was alone?"

Molly's eyes widened. "Ghosts?" she whispered.

"Don't be silly, there's no such thing as ghosts!" Max declared. "Psychic phenomena are figments of the imagination." But he glanced uneasily at Grandma.

She chuckled. "I have Baxter, don't I?" Pointed orange ears rose up over the table edge and a white paw dabbed at a scrap of Molly's bread.

Molly laughed and poked Baxter as he captured the bread. "Some bodyguard he'd be!"

After lunch, she washed the dishes while Max dried. He banished two forks back into the suds with an explanation of how many germs could live on the head of a pin. Molly rolled her eyes as she handed him the last fork. "It was your turn to wash anyhow. I did it the last time. What should we do now?"

"Let's read."

"Aw, come on!"

"Well, you could stand to practice the piano, but I'm not sure we could stand to listen."

"Comedian! Tell you what. Let's go up to the attic. Maybe I'll capture you a poltergeist."

"Never happen." Max looked out the rain-streaked window at the darkening day. Lightning flashed; thunder rumbled up the hill. The wind battered the few leaves still clinging to the branches. He turned back and grinned. "Okay, let's go. This looks like a good day for haunts. I'd be interested in something slimy and gruesome, preferably headless."

The attic was Grandma's archive. She saved things: her first doll, someone's ice skates, a 48-star flag, an elegant chair with the seat gone, a twisted cane, a crumpled hat. They all meant something to Grandma, and when she was in a sentimental mood, she could weave lively tales around them about their owners, long departed. But the family had lived in the house for generations, so, tucked away in its deepest gables, the twins sometimes found treasures from far earlier times. These musty discoveries, shrouded with dust, the twins prized most. They could challenge Max to his utmost speculations and inspire Molly to raptures of elaborate imaginings.

Filled with anticipation, they climbed the steep attic stairs and pushed the trapdoor up. Baxter dashed ahead. A dull gray-green glow entered from the narrow windows and cast the attic into a velvet gloom that stole away colors and faded out before it reached the rafters. Rain drummed on the roof. A skeletal finger of lightning probed the sky, silhouetting a bare branch clawing at a wet windowpane.

"If we wanted to scare ourselves, we came to the right place,"

said Max, a little louder than necessary. He waved his hand, searching for the light cord.

"You said there's no such thing as ghosts," Molly chided him, but mostly for her own comfort. She wasn't sure. But she did hope there was magic—for instance, an invisible force that would guide her pencil through math. She looked around at the looming attic shapes. Max caught the cord and pulled it. The swinging light shot through the dark, making grotesque shadows stalk the gloom. It danced across a trunk the twins had never noticed before.

"I think therein lives thy poltergeist!" cried Max. "Forsooth, let's have a closer look. Bring candles!"

"Why not just pull it out?" Molly replied. It was heavy, and they tugged and shoved for some time before they got it under the light. Baxter hopped up on the lid and sneezed. The trunk was the sort people took on long sea voyages. It was made of fine wood and had a high curved top, brass hinges and corners, strap handles, and a heavy brass lock that sprang open at Molly's touch. "That was too easy," she complained. "It should have been harder and more dangerous."

"Cheer up, we could all catch black lung from the dust—that would be dangerous," Max said as they raised the lid, dumping Baxter in a cloud that made them all sneeze.

"Books!" Molly's hopes fell.

"Great!" exclaimed Max, happily hefting out an enormous volume bound in marbled paper and worn leather. He laid it gently on the floor. It creaked as he opened it. "It's an anatomy book!"

"I know. Just look at the pictures," said Molly. "See, there's a person with no skin on. We had a book like that in school to show us muscles . . . only this is more detailed."

"Here's a skeleton," Max pointed, "and the digestive tract. And the arteries and veins in the circulatory system, the heart, the lungs, and the brain," he recited, proud that he could name the organs without reading the book.

"Show-off," said Molly. "Look, there's an eye, and an ear, and nerves too. And here are the cells that make them up. They look as different as the organs. The lung cells are as flat as pancakes, but the nerve cells look like spiders!"

"That's because they have different functions," Max said, turning a page.

"I know. But I have a hard time believing I really look like that on the inside." She poked her stomach doubtfully. "There's supposed to be a liver in there, but I can't feel a thing."

"That's because it's soft," said Max. "You can feel your pulse, though, and your muscles and joints and bones. See?" He made a strong-man fist.

Molly was unimpressed. "That hardly makes up for what I *can't* see. There's a whole microscopic world inside there." She returned to the trunk and began to rummage through it. Books went down to the bottom, but there, wedged in a corner, she found a small case. Inside was a delicate silver magnifying glass. Looking through it, she was surprised to see the attic shrink to the size of a dollhouse. Max looked tiny. She flipped it over and he became a giant. Inscribed with tiny words, one side said "maxify" and the other "minify."

"Hey, Max, this is crazy," she called. But he was too engrossed in turning pages to look up and only grunted a reply. Molly roamed the attic through the strange lens, flipping it over and over. Baxter purred and rubbed against them, walking on the book whenever he could, trying to trade charm for the attention he didn't get. They forgot the rain. Thunder followed lightning, and the storm rose.

"Molly, look here," Max exclaimed at last. Baxter looked up hopefully. "Remember when we had tonsillitis? Here's tonsils." He pointed to a picture of a face with a wide-open mouth. In the back of the mouth, behind the molars on either side, were two formless bulges labeled "Tonsils." Molly leaned over to examine them through her glass. Suddenly a blinding flash suspended them in brilliance. They heard a deafening boom, then darkness closed in on them. They were falling, floating, tumbling in a silent void.

Someone screamed.

9

CHAPTER TWO

In pitch dark, they landed on what felt like a bumpy wet mattress and bounced. It was silent except for the pounding of their hearts and something dripping.

"Max, are you there?" whispered Molly.

"I'm here," he whispered back. "What happened?"

"I don't know."

"Lightning must have knocked out the lights."

"And a hole in the roof, too. It's all wet. I wonder why it's so quiet." Molly wondered why she was whispering, too. The magnifying glass was still in her hand. She shoved it into her pocket and, as her eyes adjusted to the dim light, looked around. She gasped, closed her eyes, and rubbed them. Then she opened one eye at a time and looked again.

"I don't know," Max replied. "There must be some simple explanation."

"I'm not so sure. I hope you're right, but I'm scared," she said in a small voice.

"Of course I'm right. We just have to be calm until the lights come on. It sure is wet!" Max looked at Molly. She sat staring up, her eyes and mouth open wide. He looked up, following her gaze. "I don't believe this . . . ."

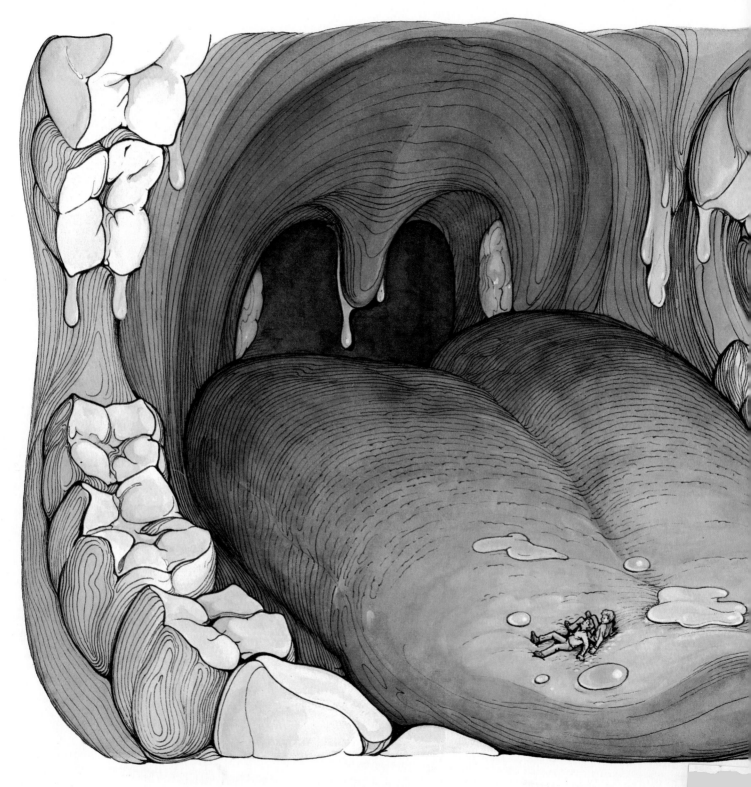

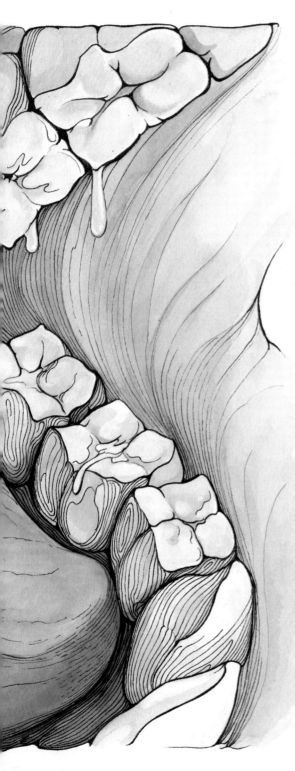

Huge teeth hung from the roof, dribbling slowly with a glistening liquid that ran down pink walls to a soft pebbly floor, which heaved and quivered under them.

"I think," Molly's voice quavered, "we are being eaten . . . by . . . a giant."

"Impossible," said Max. "There are no giants!"

"Then what do you call that?" Molly pointed at a huge tooth growing up out of the floor. It moaned. They froze in horror. "Do you suppose the giant has a toothache?" she whispered. Then something sodden, miserable, and orange crawled up onto the tooth and moaned again.

"Baxter!" cried Molly. "He's here too!"

"And about to be chewed if we don't get him off that tooth," said Max.

"Hurry!" Molly scrambled to her feet. "The water's getting deeper." They steadied each other as they tried to walk on the undulating, pebbly surface.

"This is a giant tongue!" said Max. "And this water is saliva!" They reached Baxter and pulled him to safety an instant before the teeth above came crashing down with a boom, followed by an earthquake. The tongue reared up, convulsed, and rolled to send them, slipping and sliding, toward the back of the mouth. There they were swept over a waterfall, screaming and scratching at slimy walls. The tongue, at its height, paused majestically, turned back, and rolled away, leaving them slipping farther and farther down.

"Hang on!" Max yelled. "We're being swallowed!"

"Hang on to what?" cried Molly.

Then, suddenly, there was a shelf below them. They landed on it, clung to it, and watched the flood pour over and pass into an endless tunnel below.

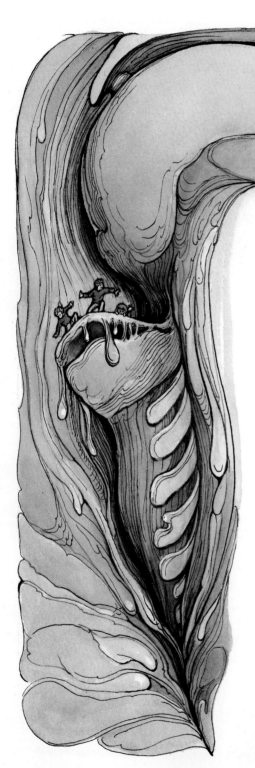

"Safe!" Max exclaimed, panting for breath, when he realized they were all on the ledge. But then it flipped up, pinning them against the wall and trapping Baxter completely behind it. He clawed himself out and had just emerged when a hurricane struck. Powerful, swirling winds snatched him from his perch and sucked him, tumbling, down a shaft below. His howl was lost in the howl of the wind. Molly screamed and grabbed for his disappearing tail, but he vanished completely. Then the wind stopped, reversed, and rose up around them in a steady breeze. The giant was breathing, Max and Molly were marooned, and Baxter was gone.

"This can't be happening!" groaned Max.

"We're trapped," Molly declared, looking up. "We could never get back up; the walls are too steep and slippery." She looked down. "We can't go down either. We'd get killed falling that far. I just hope Baxter was able to get his claws into that wall . . ."

"He always lands on his feet."

"Well, we can't. We're trapped," she repeated with finality. "Inside a giant."

"It's impossible," Max groaned again. "There has to be some logic."

"Good grief! Where's the logic in this?" She flung up a hand.

"Okay, then how do *you* explain it?"

"I was hoping you wouldn't ask me that." Molly peered down the hole after Baxter. "We have to save him."

"What? Baxter? We can't!"

"We can't just leave him there. He'll be scared out of his wits."

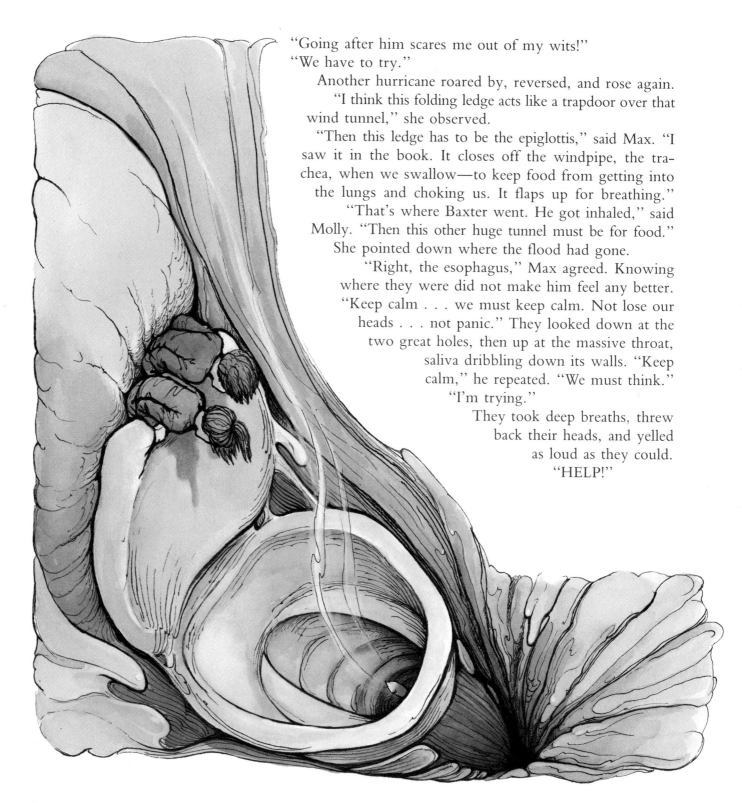

"Going after him scares me out of my wits!"

"We have to try."

Another hurricane roared by, reversed, and rose again.

"I think this folding ledge acts like a trapdoor over that wind tunnel," she observed.

"Then this ledge has to be the epiglottis," said Max. "I saw it in the book. It closes off the windpipe, the trachea, when we swallow—to keep food from getting into the lungs and choking us. It flaps up for breathing."

"That's where Baxter went. He got inhaled," said Molly. "Then this other huge tunnel must be for food." She pointed down where the flood had gone.

"Right, the esophagus," Max agreed. Knowing where they were did not make him feel any better. "Keep calm . . . we must keep calm. Not lose our heads . . . not panic." They looked down at the two great holes, then up at the massive throat, saliva dribbling down its walls. "Keep calm," he repeated. "We must think."

"I'm trying."

They took deep breaths, threw back their heads, and yelled as loud as they could.

"HELP!"

"Silence!" a small voice gurgled.

"What?" Molly looked at Max. "Did you say that?"

"Of course not. I said that. I told you to make less noise," the voice commanded. It sounded like someone trying to talk underwater.

Max looked at Molly. "Did you hear that?"

"A person would have to be deaf not to. We simply do not tolerate that kind of racket," the voice replied. No one appeared. Nothing moved except the drops of saliva slowly sliding down the walls.

They listened, holding their breath.

"That's better," declared the voice. "Now, keep quiet. Goodby."

"Wait! Don't go! We need help!" pleaded Molly.

"Take care of yourselves. Everyone else does," said the voice.

"But we're trapped! We're lost! Our cat is in terrible trouble!" Max and Molly clamored both at once, babbling frantically until the giant breathed again. Nobody heard anything until it was over.

"Hello—are you still there?" Molly called when it was quiet again.

"Gone," said Max. "We must have imagined it. It didn't even sound real."

"I'm as real as you are!" said the voice.

"Where are you?" pleaded Molly. "Will you get us out of here?"

"Don't be stupid, nobody wants out of here. This is a perfect world, Utopia. Everyone is perfectly happy," it said with finality. "No. Nobody gets in. Nobody gets out."

"Then how did we get in?" asked Max.

"How should I know? I'm not the one who's lost. I'm just where I've always been."

"Where is that?"

"Here. Where else is there?"

Max tried again. "Well, since we're here, what can we do?"

"Not much. Sooner or later the Body will eat something and wash you down."

"Down the esophagus?" gasped Molly.

"Without a doubt, unless you can fly. Can you fly?"

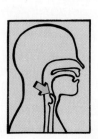

"No." She looked down the long tube and shuddered. The voice chuckled. She looked up. "I can't see you, whoever you are. Where are you, anyway?"

"Here, right under your noses!" They stared hard toward the sound and finally noticed a floating water drop. It waved.

"A tiny raindrop!" she exclaimed.

"Tiny!" said the drop. "Size is nothing to brag about around here! Besides, I can change size whenever I want. I just find this one the most convenient. And I'm certainly not rain, I'm salt water! I am the Body fluid!" he sputtered. "Tiny! Raindrop! Foof!"

"You're salty, like the ocean?" Max ventured. "I heard that body fluid is like ocean water."

"Of course. Life started in the sea. Then some foolish creatures crawled out on land without bothering to consult us, here on the Inside. They just took us for granted and dragged us along. Mind you, we were simply furious! And we certainly did not want to go! Horrible air, nasty stuff. Well, we fixed them. We brought the sea along. We got the skin to hold it in for us so it won't evaporate. And so it's been for millions of years."

"Amazing," mused Max. "You built yourself a house of skin to keep the dry out, just like our houses keep the rain out." He had a sudden lonely thought of the rain drumming on the sturdy attic roof of Grandma's house. It seemed millions of years ago.

"Yes, we did," said the drop. "And a fine house it is."

"If that all happened so long ago, how do you know so much about it?" Molly asked.

"I was there, of course."

"Are you that old?"

"Quite. I pass on from generation to generation. All Bodies have come from the first one. I just happened to end up here." The drop floated before them, waving tiny arms in elaborate gestures as it spoke. To make particular points, it would shake its head and fists so hard that flecks of water flipped off, giving

it the ever disinte-
grating appearance
of a lawn sprinkler.
Then it would have to brush
up next to a dribble of saliva, merge
with it, replenish itself, and start all
over again, discoursing, gesticulating,
and sprinkling. Molly saw how this
process could go on forever.

"By the way, my name is Freewilly, because I
am free to go everywhere in the Body. My liquid
constitution allows me to flow in and around all the
cells. I'm into everything. But I didn't catch your
names."

"I'm Max and this is Molly. We had a cat with us, but
he got sucked into the lungs."

"We're kids," Molly added, "and we're lost from our grandmother's attic. We would like very much to find our cat and go
back there. Do you know how?"

"My, my, you *are* lost, aren't you?" Freewilly looked them
over. "Where might grandmother's attic be?"

"In the outside world," Max replied. This had an immediate
effect on Freewilly. He lost several sizable drops. "Can you
help us?"

"Certainly not! What blasphemy! Nobody gets out! Why,
one of our biggest problems is to keep them from getting in!
Germs, viruses, riffraff," he sputtered. "If it weren't for our
fine skin, we'd be overrun. Forget that, nobody leaves."

"Would you at least help us find our cat?" Molly asked.
"Will you take us to the lungs?"

"Well, I suppose." He considered them again, doubtfully.
"So you are little lost humans, are you? This could be most
interesting after all. Some company would be nice in my
travels—most of the cells are stuck down, you know." He re-
plenished himself with a large drop before going on. "Just forget that nonsense about getting out, attics, and grandmothers.
You'll love it here once you get used to it."

Max opened his mouth, then shut it again.

Molly whispered to him, "Let's find Baxter and then worry
about getting out."

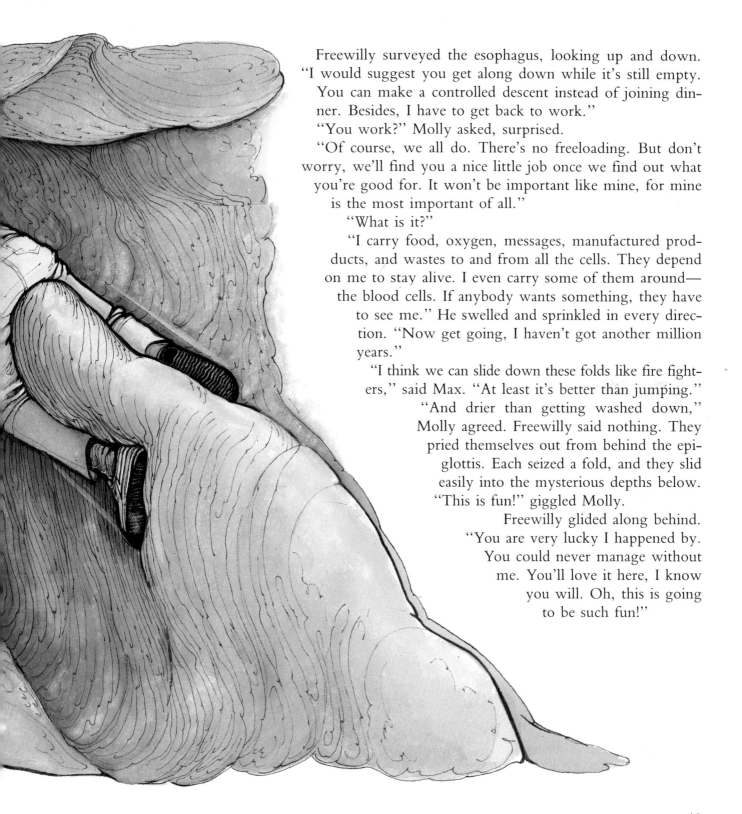

Freewilly surveyed the esophagus, looking up and down. "I would suggest you get along down while it's still empty. You can make a controlled descent instead of joining dinner. Besides, I have to get back to work."

"You work?" Molly asked, surprised.

"Of course, we all do. There's no freeloading. But don't worry, we'll find you a nice little job once we find out what you're good for. It won't be important like mine, for mine is the most important of all."

"What is it?"

"I carry food, oxygen, messages, manufactured products, and wastes to and from all the cells. They depend on me to stay alive. I even carry some of them around—the blood cells. If anybody wants something, they have to see me." He swelled and sprinkled in every direction. "Now get going, I haven't got another million years."

"I think we can slide down these folds like fire fighters," said Max. "At least it's better than jumping."

"And drier than getting washed down," Molly agreed. Freewilly said nothing. They pried themselves out from behind the epiglottis. Each seized a fold, and they slid easily into the mysterious depths below. "This is fun!" giggled Molly.

Freewilly glided along behind. "You are very lucky I happened by. You could never manage without me. You'll love it here, I know you will. Oh, this is going to be such fun!"

CHAPTER THREE

The fun ended. The esophagus emptied into a hot, snarling sea churning in a writhing cave. The walls of the cave pounded and twisted and rubbed together, grinding the sea into violent waves and drizzling it with stinging fluid. The twins dumped in with a splash. Max bobbed up, yelled, "Stomach!" and saw Molly paddling furiously to escape the surging and plunging of a half-chewed unidentifiable chunk of something beige. A wave washed over his head. He came up choking, eyes burning. "Acid!" he cried. Molly was now being pursued by something soft and red. She caught sight of a lettuce leaf floating on the surface and swam for it. "Max! Over here!" Together they captured the leaf and dragged themselves up on it. Freewilly, dancing lightly just above the waves, laughed so hard he nearly fell apart.

"It's not funny!" cried Max, wiping his eyes. "That's acid!"

"Oh, not entirely!" Freewilly giggled. "It's digestive juice—a sort of hot soup. There are lots of things in it besides acid. Why, there's even saliva in that recipe. The stomach squeezes, drizzles, and chomps, but it's the juice that really digests the food. I'm partial to juices. Isn't this magnificent?" He gestured expansively, sprinkling liberally, and took a bow. A chunk of radish crashed into the leaf boat as a surge of waves nearly capsized it. A curl of acid soup slopped up into their faces.

"OW!" cried Max. "This acid is eating us up!"

"It's not nearly as strong as it could be," Freewilly blithely assured him. "It's quite diluted by lunch, and there's some milk in there too. That should have neutralized some acid by now. It could be a lot worse."

"Lucky for us," Molly grumbled as she wiped her face.

"Besides," said Freewilly, "it's killing germs."

"Terrific," said Max. "We may drown or get mashed to pieces, but at least we'll be sanitary."

"I knew this place reminded me of something," Molly remarked. "It's like going through a car wash."

"Only without the car," Max replied.

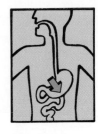

Freewilly flipped a few drops. "Is that all you can do, whine and complain? Come on, let's get out of here."

"There's no way out," said Molly, "I already looked. The walls go all the way around."

"There's a gate down at the other end."

"Why didn't you say so?" Max sighed.

"Paddle!" Molly commanded, plunging her arm over the side. Using their arms as oars, they rowed their boat toward the far end of the stomach. "Look, there's slime all over the walls," she said.

"It protects them from their own acid," said Freewilly. "Otherwise, the stomach would digest itself."

"That would be some stomachache," said Max.

"We should have smeared some of it on us. But then we'd still be covered with germs." Molly wiped her forehead. "It's hot!"

"It's 98.6 degrees, I'd guess," said Max.

22

"I hope the giant doesn't get a fever."

"I think I'm getting seasick." They rounded a bend and could see to the end of the stomach, but nothing there resembled a gate. It was only a great puckering—a dead end. Max looked accusingly at Freewilly, who only smiled, dripped, and waited. Soon a small hole appeared and expanded in the center of the puckered wall. The writhing stomach walls organized and squeezed. Clinging to their leaf, the twins squirted through the hole, rolled over some rapids, and splashed down into a quiet river. There they lay and panted for a while, floating in a tubular tunnel under arching red walls.

"The small intestine," said Freewilly, waving at the long tunnel. "Peristalsis," he said when the tunnel walls squeezed behind them, pumping them along. "You won't have to paddle anymore."

They glided in a peaceful silence broken only by occasional drips. "Are you seasick, Max? You look green," said Molly.

"Thanks," he replied. "That helps a lot. I'll be okay. It was the rough ride." He smiled a game but queasy smile.

"It's lucky nothing much is going on around here," Molly observed, also grateful for the respite.

"There's plenty going on," said Freewilly. "It's just not as dramatic as in the stomach. The small intestine is finishing up digestion before it puts food in the blood."

"Where's the blood?" Molly looked around. She could see only soft, red, velvet arches and a river of food.

"Oh, it's a little hard to see from here," Freewilly replied, then pointed. "Look." A green waterfall splashed into the river.

"That's not blood," said Molly.

"It's more digestive juice, come to finish the job," Freewilly explained. "Some comes from the pancreas gland on the other side of the wall, but some comes all the way from the liver by pipeline." He flung some drops above and behind them.

"I remember where the liver is," Molly volunteered, poking her stomach.

"Why is the waterfall green?" Max asked, as he watched its ripples spread toward them. "The bile from the liver is green. It dissolves fat, grease, butter, oil." They drifted on through the small intestine, through loops and twists under endless arches on an endless river. Molly was still waiting to see the blood, when she suddenly felt wet seeping through the leaf. "We're sinking!" she shrieked. "Our leaf is full of holes!" They began paddling for shore.

"There must have been salad oil protecting it," Max shouted. "The bile dissolved the oil, and the juices got through." Freewilly clapped gleefully. "I wondered when you would figure that out." The twins scrambled onto the soft red bank.

Molly gave Freewilly an accusing look. "You might have warned us."

"It was much more exciting this way," he giggled. "Don't you think?"

"Well, now what?" demanded Max. "Some guide you are!"

Freewilly sniffed. "I didn't do anything. You could have gone on into the large intestine. That's where you were headed, and, fussy as you are, you wouldn't have liked that very much! That's where wastes are stored."

"That's true," Molly said resignedly, "but you should have told us just the same." She gazed at the disintegrating leaf. "Thank you, old boat. I will remember you with every salad."

"I wonder when we'll see another salad," Max said sadly. "Or Baxter . . . or get out."

"We'd better stop thinking like that or we'll get depressed."

"You're right—if we get through this, it will be through clear and logical thinking."

"And keeping our eyes and ears open."

"At least we're sanitary." He flicked his sleeve with a finger. "Where's Freewilly?'

"He's gone up that hill. He's waving for us to come." They started after him.

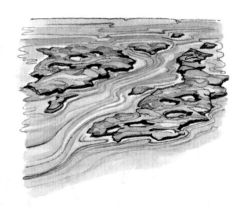

The wall of the small intestine was lined with a fuzzy, slightly sticky red carpet with no openings, no puckering holes, and no way out. Freewilly sat perched on a lump, smiling innocently and twiddling two watery thumbs. "Gee, he's gotten a lot bigger—I just noticed," Molly said suddenly.

"Hey, you're right. But he said he could change size. He must have done it gradually, or we would have seen it."

"But it's not just Freewilly. When we got on our leaf, it could barely hold us, and just now, even falling apart, it was enormous. The leaf couldn't get bigger! We're getting . . . smaller." They stared at each other in dismay. "How small do you suppose . . . ?"

"That's not all!" said Max. "I'm having trouble walking. I can hardly drag my feet along." They stopped and looked down. Their feet were stuck and sinking into the soft fur. The more they struggled to get free, the deeper they sank, up to their knees, waists, chests, chins . . . and astonished eyes. The red carpet folded silently over Max's reaching hand, and they were gone. Freewilly sat chuckling until they sank from sight, then he floated up, stretched himself thin, and slid through the wall. The leaf sank slowly in the river of food, the walls squeezed, and the river flowed on.

CHAPTER FOUR

Max and Molly floated down. Lights flashed by, currents flowed around them; they were bumped, buffeted, and popped into a flooded tunnel.

"Good grief, we're drowning!" cried Max.

"No, we're not! I can breathe! Try it!"

Max sniffed tentatively, then took a breath. He was actually breathing underwater. "Are you okay?" he asked.

She nodded. "What happened?"

"I don't know, it was too fast! I got sucked into something, then I was here!"

"Where are we? What happened to Freewilly?" Molly looked around. "Everything's red!" A current tugged at her clothes.

"Look!" He pointed up the tube. A pack of fat red disks careened toward them, tumbling as they came. "Those are red blood cells. Just like in the book! We're in the blood!" They pressed themselves against the curved wall, trying to get out of the way.

"I kept wondering where the blood was," Molly said. "Freewilly said that's where the food goes. Are we still shrinking?" She scrutinized her hand.

"I can't tell. There's nothing to compare."

"Oh, what will we do? I wish Freewilly would come," Molly whimpered.

"He's no help! The worse it gets, the more he enjoys it. He won't tell us anything useful. And we're nowhere near the lungs. We'll never find Baxter!"

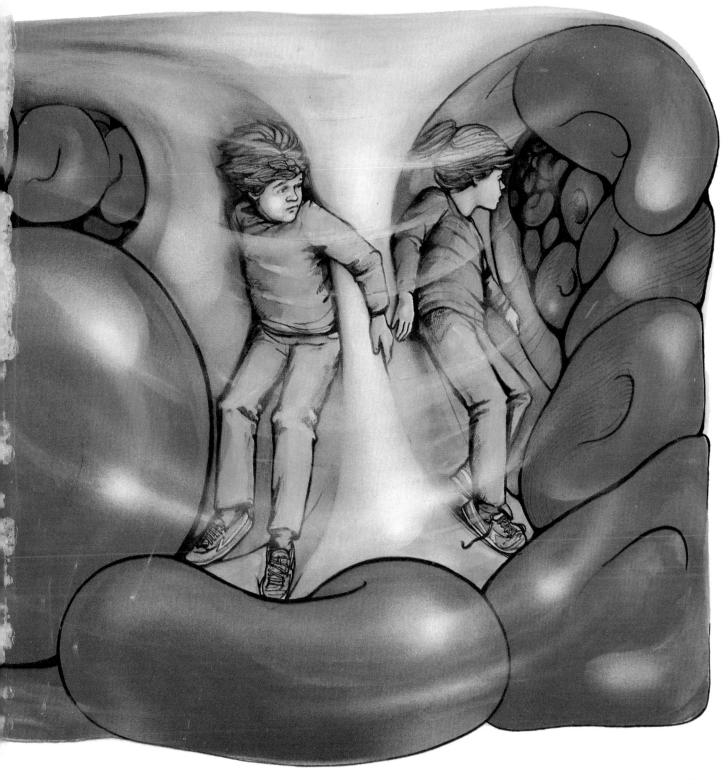

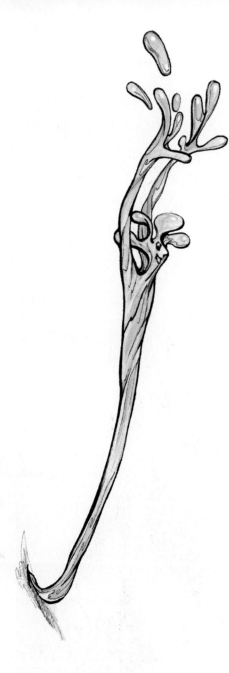

"I still wish he'd come. At least we can breathe in here."

"Of course you can!" Thin as an eel, Freewilly slid through the wall. "Those red cells are giving you some of their oxygen. With my help, naturally, they haul oxygen to the cells and trade it in for carbon dioxide. How did you like being absorbed?"

"Now you tell us! Couldn't you please say something before it happens?" Max complained.

"Look, Max, Freewilly's the same size! We're not shrinking anymore.'

"That's some consolation," he grumbled. "Where are we, anyway?"

"In a capillary, the smallest of blood vessels," Freewilly said, flourishing a hand. "It's full of blood and wonderfully wet! The big arteries fan out into millions of these capillaries, and they weave all around carrying blood into every little corner. Spreading the blood out also slows it down, so it has time to do its business with the cells. This blood here is picking up the dissolved food from the intestine, with my help, of course. My fluid makes all this possible. Oh, it's hard to be humble when I look around."

"Excuse me." A red blood cell had gotten turned sideways and was nearly stuck in the narrow vessel. It rubbed them against the wall and barely squeezed by.

"We're causing a traffic jam," said Molly. A long line of cells waited behind and, one by one, they nudged the twins against the wall.

"I think you'd better move along," one of them said to Molly. It nodded and bobbled beside her. "You're about to cause a clot. This capillary is one-way, no parking, no stopping, no standing. Where are you trying to go?"

Molly stammered in surprise, "To the lungs. To get our cat. Do you know the way?"

"Of course I do. If you ride the blood, sooner or later you'll get there. The blood goes everywhere."

"Wait a minute, that's not so!" said Freewilly. "There's places I go that you never heard of! Now I'm with these two, so you go on about your business."

"Freewilly, you haven't been the greatest help so far," Max pointed out.

"Foof!" Freewilly pouted.

The red cell studied Molly, then remarked, "You don't float very well, do you?"

"Not at all!" She held up her arm. "My clothes are all soggy and my shoes are full of water . . . or something." She squished her shoes to demonstrate.

"Well, come on, I'll give you a lift. I'll see if my buddy behind will carry that other one. We certainly have to get you out of here."

Freewilly, sulking, was soon cheered by their futile attempts to mount and ride red blood cells. Molly sat down on hers. "Like an inner tube," she instructed Max, only to be flipped and dumped. Freewilly laughed and Max had to smile. Then he tried and ended in similar disgrace. Freewilly somersaulted with glee. Eventually they tried turning the cells on edge and straddling them.

"It's like riding ponies," said Max, "except the ponies don't seem to care whether they're rightside up or otherwise."

"Hey!" a voice called from far behind in the line of cells. "What's holding you up? We're about to clot!" More grumbling echoed the call. As soon as the twins' feet left the ground, the force of the blood shoved them off. They were flushed along, occasionally bumping into walls, rolling, and colliding with other cells that popped into their tunnel from other tunnels forming a fantastic, tumbling maze. Max, clinging to his cell, looked back over his shoulder to see their long red line. When he turned around, Molly and Freewilly, who had been just in front of him, were gone. They had turned up another tunnel in the maze, and he was alone.

"I'm lost," he moaned.

"You can't get lost," his red cell said, giving him a start, for it hadn't spoken until now. "We go to the liver next, to drop off the food. Then we go to the heart."

"Oh," Max moaned again. "We have to get to the lungs."

"No problem, the lungs are just beyond the heart—you can't miss them."

"Do all cells talk?"

"Only when we want to, and then only if we're close by. I've heard tell of some cells that talk from one end of the Body to the other, but they must have louder voices than we do.

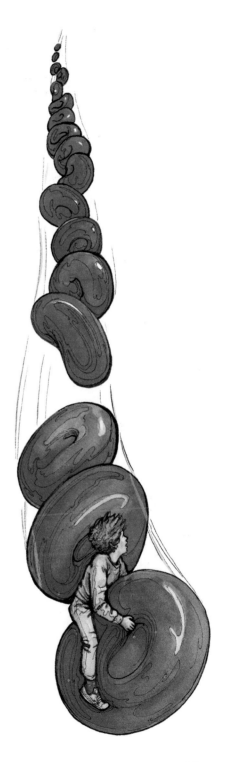

There are the hormones, too, which travel around in the blood. They're chemical messengers made in the glands. We meet them riding around looking for the cells that can read them. But they don't talk to us."

"Can you call up the red cell that Molly's riding so I can find her?"

"No need to. She'll be along directly. All the capillaries are coming together now to make a vein. This is the circulatory system, we travel around and around. By the way, I've never seen anyone like you before. Are you traveling on business?"

"You might say that. We're looking for a cat," Max replied. "Then we're going home."

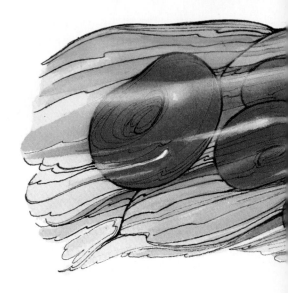

The red cell considered this information. He knew little about the rest of the Body, but he had heard that it had mysterious ways and important functions, and that others sometimes had strange, exotic assignments. His own job, although surely the most important, did get boring. He dreamed of adventure. This strange creature obviously had a rare and delicate mission, identified by code words. "Kat," he whispered in secret excitement, then spoke to Max in a low, conspiratorial tone. "Top secret? Don't say another word. Trust me—I'll get you there." Suddenly Molly, on her red cell, burst in from another vein and collided with them. They were all traveling much faster now, as the vessels got larger.

"Am I ever glad to see you!" she exclaimed. "Where were you?"

"We took a wrong turn. Where's Freewilly?"

She tossed her head. "Back there, having the time of his life. He thought it was hilarious when you got lost."

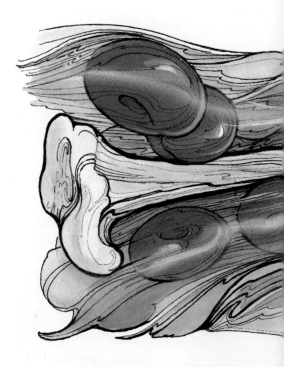

The vein grew to enormous size and the blood rushed them, tumbling, into the liver. Then the vessels began dividing again, and the blood slowed down until they were once more traveling in small channels.

"This is where the liver takes the food out of the body," Molly's cell told them.

"To make the bile?" Molly asked.

"Yes!" Freewilly appeared from nowhere and hurried to answer, giving the cell a hateful glance. "The liver makes bile, but it mostly stores the food, releasing a little at a time as the Body needs it. It also decontaminates its toxins and poisons."

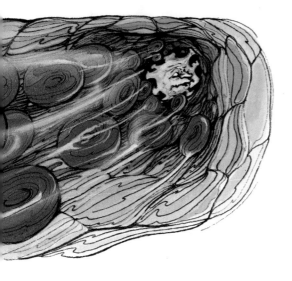

"Poison!" exclaimed Molly. "Was there poison in that lunch?"

"Probably some," Freewilly expounded. "There are lots of things that we call poisons—alcohol is one. Lucky for us this liver is here to sop them up and demolish them." As he chattered and flourished, he glanced ahead. Suddenly he seemed to lose his train of thought and fell behind. The two red cells whispered to each other. Max looked ahead and yelped. Something enormous, resembling an octopus, blocked the tunnel.

"What is that?" asked Molly.

"A liver guard," her red cell replied. "He's a white blood cell of the defense system. He's looking for invaders. You have your identification, don't you?"

"Freewilly!" Max turned just in time to see Freewilly slipping away through the wall. "Hey!" he called. Freewilly didn't seem to hear, but Max saw him glance back, furtively, before he disappeared.

They were fast approaching the white cell. "What does he do with invaders when he catches them?" Molly asked.

"Eats them," her cell replied. "When they get a big one, they wrap around it and dissolve it slowly." Molly gulped, staring at the massive creature. His many feet were planted around the tunnel, suspending his hulk across their path. He poked little waving arms from his sides, snagging an unfortunate little creature that had floated too close. He slurped it into his great wobbling mouth, munched, savored it, and smiled. Then he rolled his goggle eyes in their direction, slurped again, and roared.

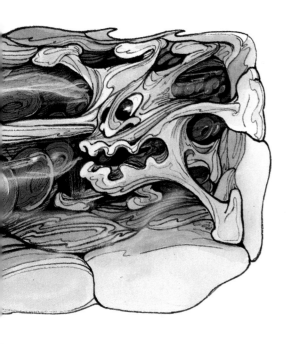

"Strangers! Halt and be recognized." Max and Molly shrank down on the backs of their round red friends.

"Don't worry," whispered Max's cell. "We'll get you through. We're going to make a run for it." But fast as a snake, the great cell reached out, caught them, and held them fast.

"Hey, you big thug, let me go!" Molly's cell yelled. The white cell ignored him and bulged his eyes at the twins.

"Now! Now! What have we here?" he boomed. "Are you my dessert? I like dessert." He extended a nose and took a little sniff. His eyes goggled. "My, my, the Body is eating peculiar these days." A small creature fled past. With incredible swiftness, he snagged it and tossed it in his mouth. He drooled,

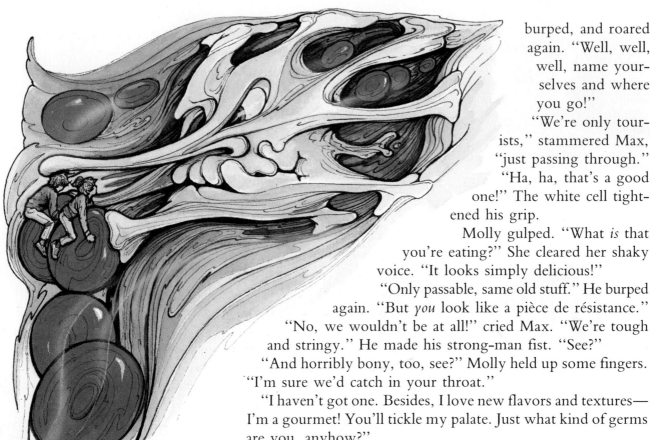

burped, and roared again. "Well, well, well, name your-selves and where you go!"

"We're only tour-ists," stammered Max, "just passing through."

"Ha, ha, that's a good one!" The white cell tight-ened his grip.

Molly gulped. "What *is* that you're eating?" She cleared her shaky voice. "It looks simply delicious!"

"Only passable, same old stuff." He burped again. "But *you* look like a pièce de résistance."

"No, we wouldn't be at all!" cried Max. "We're tough and stringy." He made his strong-man fist. "See?"

"And horribly bony, too, see?" Molly held up some fingers. "I'm sure we'd catch in your throat."

"I haven't got one. Besides, I love new flavors and textures—I'm a gourmet! You'll tickle my palate. Just what kind of germs are you, anyhow?"

"We're *kids!*" cried Max.

"Wonderful, a new flavor." The mouth stretched to accom-modate them.

"Wait!" Molly cried. "If we were germs, we'd smell like germs, wouldn't we? Well, take a sniff! That's what your nose is for, isn't it?" She bit her lip and held her breath, and hoped the stomach had sanitized them well. A long, rubbery nose snaked out and patted over them, sniffing.

"Well, well, you don't smell like germs, at least not like any I've been told to catch . . . . But you do smell familiar."

Molly took another wild chance. "Of course we do, we're human. Like this Body." Then it struck her that she couldn't be sure it was a human body. Were giants human? Maybe it was another animal altogether. She had no way of knowing.

The great white cell pulled itself up sharply. "Human! Why didn't you say so? My job is to protect Human. I work in the defense system. Is this some kind of security check? I'm on the job, as you can see, ready to eat germs!"

"Then it wouldn't do to eat us, would it?" Molly demanded. "You've passed with flying colors. Now let us go, and carry on."

"How was I to know?" asked the monster cell. "I never saw Humans before. They never tell us anything down here."

"It's quite all right," Molly allowed. "Anyone can make a mistake."

"It won't happen again," promised the cell, releasing them and rolling his bulk around in the tunnel to watch them sail away. He produced a brand-new arm from his back side to salute them with. "So that's a Human," he murmured, turning back to his work. "I thought they would be much better looking."

As soon as they were out of sight, Max's red cell exclaimed, "We did it! That was wonderful! Brilliant! It was so exciting. The mission is saved! I'm so proud to be part of all this. You must be their very best secret agents!"

Max beamed proudly. "Molly, that was terrific. I never would have thought of that."

"It wasn't very logical, that's why. It didn't even make much sense. Security check! I was only bluffing." She shrugged. "What does he mean by secret agents?"

"*I'll* say that was good thinking!" Freewilly's voice came through the wall and he gaily followed it. "We handled that very well!"

Max gave him a sour look. "Gee thanks, you helped a lot. We couldn't have done it without you."

"Don't mention it."

CHAPTER FIVE

We're leaving the liver," Freewilly announced, positioning himself between Max and Molly, "and that's why we're picking up speed. Notice the veins coming together all around us. Soon we'll be in the biggest vein of all, the inferior vena cava—which doesn't mean it's not as good as the superior vena cava. It just means it's bringing up the blood from below the heart. The superior vena cava brings down blood from above the heart." He rattled on until they couldn't hear him anymore. Submerged in the sound of a thundering, rhythmic pounding, they swept into the heart.

34

Red blood cells tumbled all around them, rolling and shrieking with glee.

"Hooray! Whoopee! Whee!" they called to each other in joyful anticipation.

"There's no way out!" shouted Max over the din. Then a white wall bulging toward them sprang apart into three triangular flaps that snapped aside, uncovering a gigantic pit. Max and Molly and their two red cells and everyone rejoicing in the round chamber were instantly sucked into that pit. They caught glimpses of twisted, gnarled forms writhing on its walls before they crashed against them. Just then, the walls contracted with a resounding BOOM,

BOOM

rushing together and shooting them upward again in a violent red blur into another great vessel some distance away. They nearly lost sight of each other through the red flood.

"Holy cow!" exclaimed Max. "That must have been a heartbeat!" Freewilly, piecing himself together again nearby, nodded confirmation.

Molly's red cell, altogether jubilant, asked, "Wasn't that exhilarating?" as she unburied her nose from his back.

"That word hardly seems adequate," she mumbled.

"I knew you'd love it! It's one of the high points of our trip. I don't mean to complain; the Body couldn't live without us red cells, but our job does get a little boring. We go around and around all the time. Go to the lungs, pick up oxygen; go to the cells, drop off the oxygen, pick up carbon dioxide; back to the lungs, drop off the carbon dioxide. So it goes, never a day off. I do so look forward to these two trips through the heart on every circuit—they give my life some pizzazz!"

THE CIRCULATORY SYSTEM

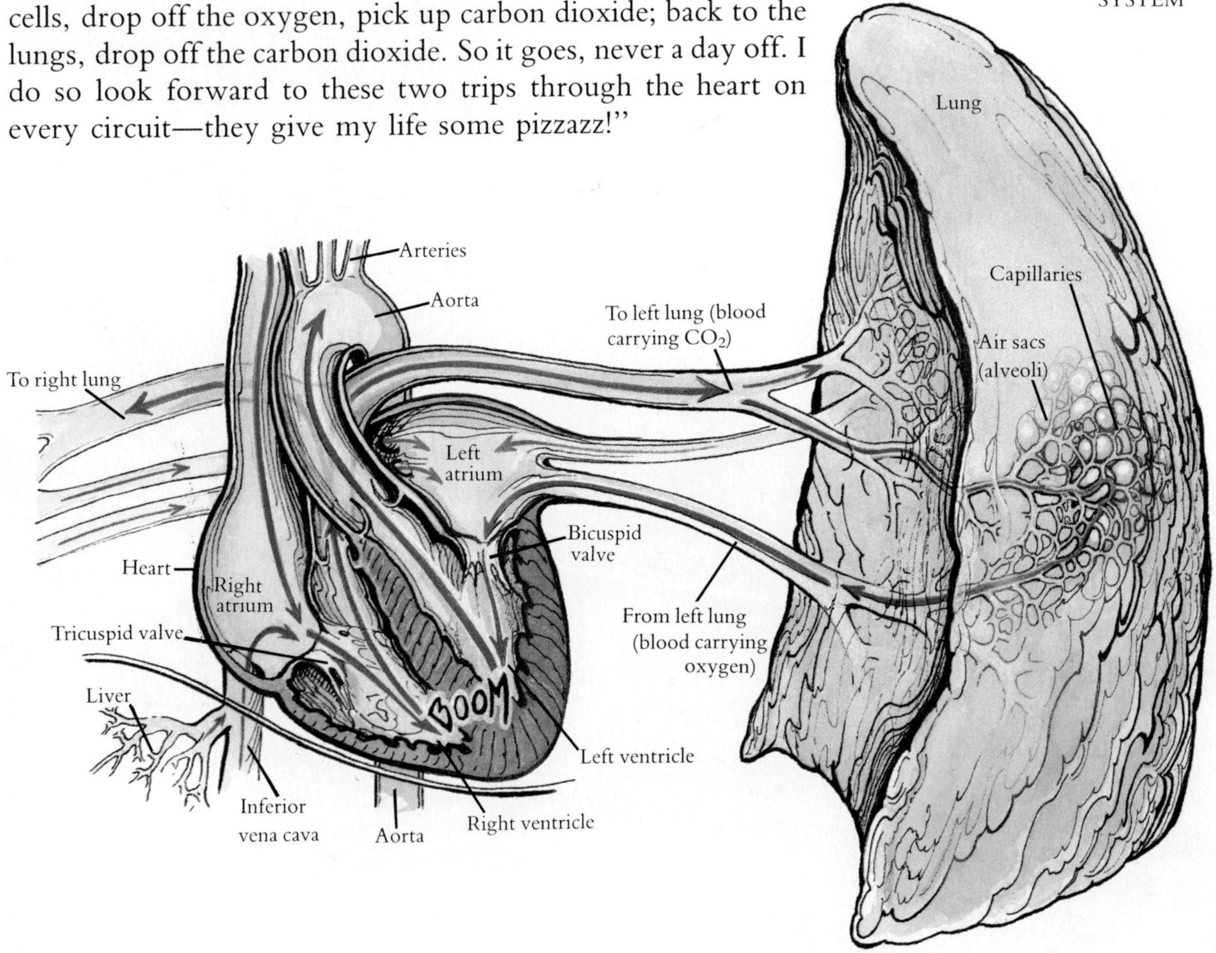

Lung

Capillaries

Air sacs (alveoli)

Arteries

Aorta

To left lung (blood carrying CO_2)

Left atrium

Bicuspid valve

Heart

Right atrium

To right lung

From left lung (blood carrying oxygen)

Tricuspid valve

Liver

GOOM

Left ventricle

Inferior vena cava

Aorta

Right ventricle

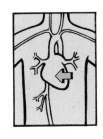

"Two trips!" said Molly. "Have we gotta go through that again?"

"Not you, we're dropping you off. You wanted to go to the lungs, and they're coming up."

"Thank goodness."

"That back there was the right side of the heart. It only gives us enough go-power to get to the lungs and back. After that, we go through the left side to get boosted out to the rest of the Body. That's where the real power is, the left heart. Why, it can pump me all the way down to the toes—and up again. It's a real thrill."

Max and Freewilly floated up. "Let's all stick together now." Freewilly directed. "More capillaries ahead." Then to Molly's cell: "What were you talking about?"

"I was telling about our circulations."

"Foof!" said Freewilly, and shot him a withering glance.

"Did you see that white wall split apart?" Max asked the cells.

"That was the tricuspid valve," said Freewilly, before either cell could answer. "It has three flaps. They separate to let blood flow from the right atrium into the right ventricle." He rushed on, drawing pictures with his hands. "The atrium gathers up blood from the veins and dumps it into the ventricle. The ventricle is all muscle, and it squeezes to pump the blood out through an artery. The valve opens and closes the door between the atrium and ventricle and keeps the blood flowing in one direction. Otherwise, it would just slosh back and forth, and the Body would starve to death."

"One-way valves," said Max. "We have them on the Outside too."

"Surely not as fine as ours. There's another big valve between the left atrium and ventricle. Since it only has two flaps, we call it the bicuspid valve. Then there's a valve apiece in the great arteries leaving the heart."

"There are also lots of valves in the veins of the legs and trunk," ventured Molly's cell. "They help us climb up a little at a time, from valve to valve."

"Like a ladder," said Max.

"I was just going to mention them," said Freewilly.

"By the way, where are we now?" asked Max.

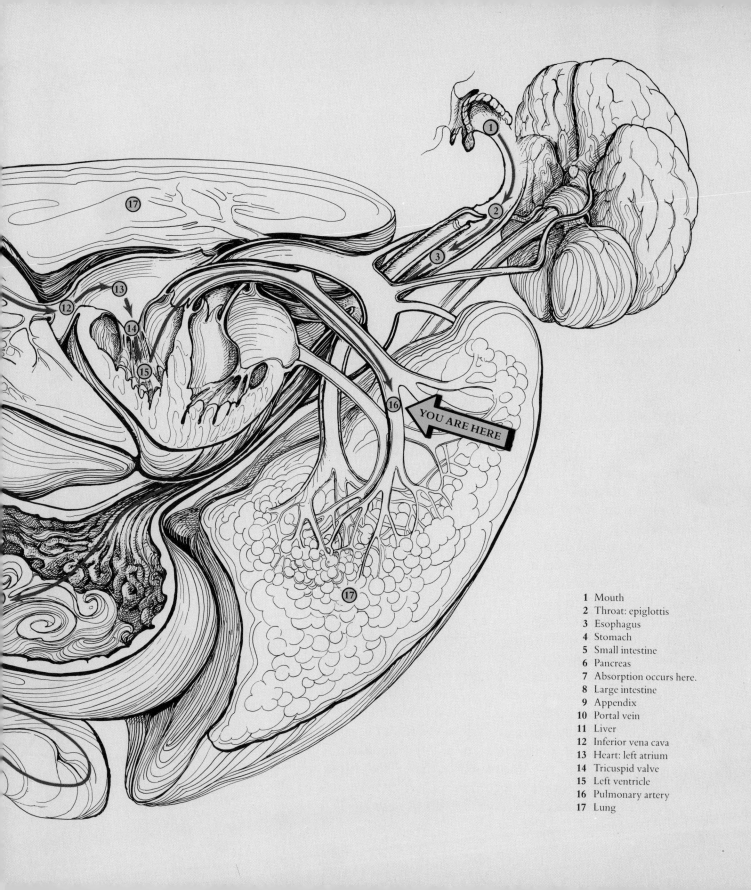

YOU ARE HERE

1 Mouth
2 Throat: epiglottis
3 Esophagus
4 Stomach
5 Small intestine
6 Pancreas
7 Absorption occurs here.
8 Large intestine
9 Appendix
10 Portal vein
11 Liver
12 Inferior vena cava
13 Heart: left atrium
14 Tricuspid valve
15 Left ventricle
16 Pulmonary artery
17 Lung

"In an artery going to the lungs," said Molly, "so we'd better start looking for Baxter."

"The lungs are simply enormous," said Freewilly. "How do you propose to go about this expedition?"

"Aren't you going to lead us to him?" Molly looked up. "You said you would." They were slowing down toward the capillaries.

"I never did! I hate lungs, they're full of dust and *air*. Heaven forbid, I never go in there. I said I'd get you here, that's all."

"But without you, how can we ever find him?" Molly pleaded.

"Who ever said you could? The lungs are packed with millions of sacs of air, and he could be in any one of them. This is only the left lung, the right one is back there and just as big." He tossed a hand behind.

Max groaned and wondered if it was all right to sock a water drop.

"You're just trying to discourage us so we'll give up and stay," declared Molly. "Well, it won't work!"

Freewilly threw her an arch glance. "You'll see. Better hurry, here are the capillaries. Pick an air sac—there are millions around." Then he floated away without saying goodby.

"Good riddance!" said Max. "He's impossible!"

Molly dismounted from her cell. "Hey, you're blushing," she said.

"I'm picking up my load of oxygen and that always brightens me up," he explained. "I carry hemoglobin molecules inside me that attract the oxygen from the air just outside that wall. If you want to go into the lung, open a slot between the cells of the capillary wall. Goodby, and good luck."

Max's cell vigorously regretted being left behind. "The best of luck," he encouraged. "The mission is now in your capable hands." He was glowing bright red and nearly bursting to spread their story all over the Body. Then he was boosted away amid loud complaints from other cells lined up behind.

Max and Molly tugged apart a slot in the seam between two pancake-like cells that wrapped around the capillary. They stepped through and the slot closed behind them. More flat cells, another slot, and they stepped into a spherical room filled with fog and air. They took deep breaths.

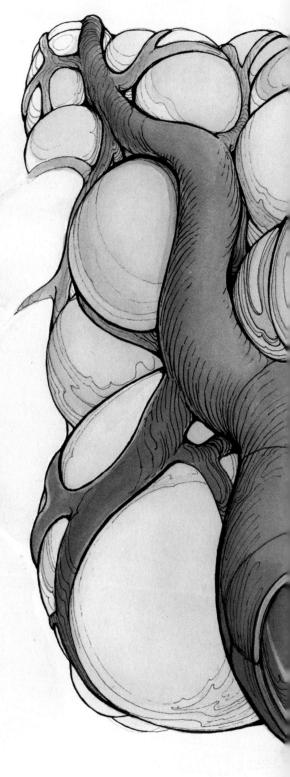

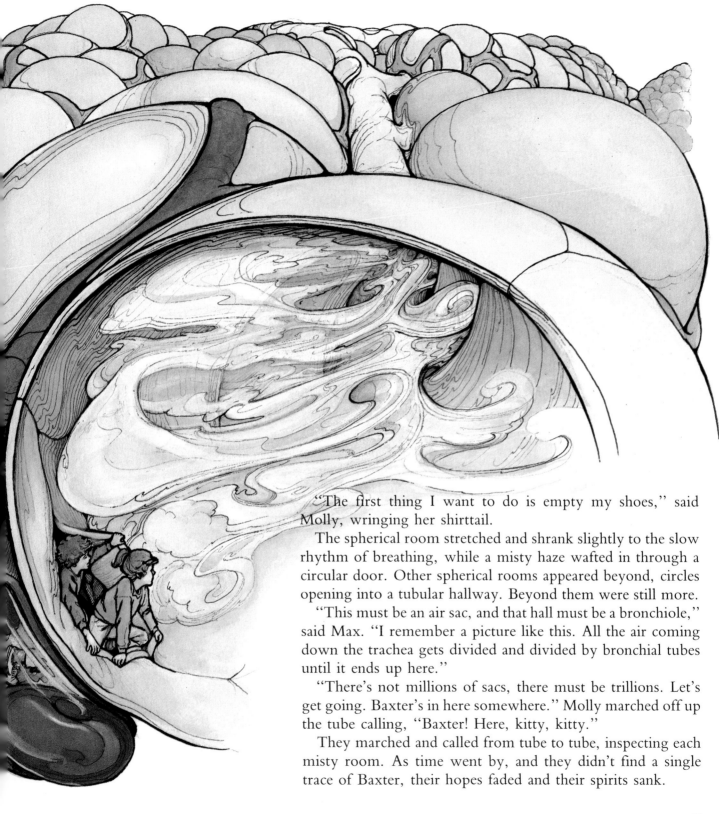

"The first thing I want to do is empty my shoes," said Molly, wringing her shirttail.

The spherical room stretched and shrank slightly to the slow rhythm of breathing, while a misty haze wafted in through a circular door. Other spherical rooms appeared beyond, circles opening into a tubular hallway. Beyond them were still more.

"This must be an air sac, and that hall must be a bronchiole," said Max. "I remember a picture like this. All the air coming down the trachea gets divided and divided by bronchial tubes until it ends up here."

"There's not millions of sacs, there must be trillions. Let's get going. Baxter's in here somewhere." Molly marched off up the tube calling, "Baxter! Here, kitty, kitty."

They marched and called from tube to tube, inspecting each misty room. As time went by, and they didn't find a single trace of Baxter, their hopes faded and their spirits sank.

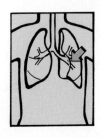

"This is stupid," Max said finally. "We've been at this for hours. Baxter's probably having a wonderful time 50 miles from here. He never comes when he's called anyway."

"He's probably sound asleep and not listening. He's a champion at naps."

"We could tramp around forever and never find him. We could even be going around in circles."

"Or spheres."

"Bad joke."

"We've just got to find him!" Molly sat down, footsore and weary and close to tears.

"Maybe he left the lung and got into the blood," Max suggested, heaving a sigh and sitting down beside her.

"No, he'd never get wet willingly. He has to be here."

"Where? Look at us, we're exhausted and still haven't found a clue. We're no closer to getting out than before. This is a big waste of time."

"At least we're dry," said Molly weakly. "I'm sure when we find him, everything will be okay."

"Do you think some magic is just going to transport us back into the attic?"

"Something like that."

"That's dumb. We have to find a logical explanation. Maybe this is all a dream, and we'll wake up."

"Some dream. More like a nightmare. Besides, who ever heard of two people having the same exact dream? This is real. I wonder if Freewilly is right and nobody ever gets out."

"He also says nobody wants to. He doesn't want us to get out. He wants to keep us here forever."

"Can you imagine a lifetime listening to his lectures? He keeps going on about how great it is, and I just want to go home. I'd give anything to be back in Grandma's kitchen. Maybe eating that dessert . . . . Why, I'm so hungry, I'd even gladly eat the soup." Her eyes brimmed over.

"Stop crying. If you start talking like that, I'll start, and then we'll both be too miserable to think. We have to stop whining."

"I know. I can't think when I'm whining. I'm just so mad at Freewilly for not taking care of us."

"Well, he's gone and he wouldn't help us if he could, so just stop all that and grow up."

"Me grow up! I'm not the one who goes around pretending to be so smart, analyzing everything and still not coming up with any answers."

"At least I don't think some fairy godmother is going to come hoofing through this lung to save us!" They glared at each other.

Molly sighed. "We're arguing again, and that's not going to help. Let's drop it and try to cooperate for once." They sat in silence.

Max sighed. "I'll make you a deal. I'll stop if you stop."

"Okay."

They sat thinking. Then Max spoke. "The way I see it, there are four possibilities. We find Baxter and get out, we find Baxter and don't get out, we don't find Baxter and get out, or we don't find Baxter and don't get out."

"You just promised! I knew it, you can't stop!"

"Huh? Oh, well, it's going to take practice. But just the same, what do you think of the possibilities?"

"Terrific. One out of four."

"That's not what I mean. What I'm saying is, there's no way to tell. There are so many things we can't know. What happens, happens."

"Do you mean give up?"

"No, but we can't do any better than our best."

"And the rest is really up to chance?"

"That's it."

"With a little brains . . ." Molly smiled.

"And a little luck . . ." Max smiled. "Anyway, we might as well have a good look around. Here we are, smack in the middle of a living human body, and we have the chance of a lifetime to see how it works."

"Come to think of it, we're lucky. Just think how smart we'll be when we get back in health class."

"That's the spirit!" Max grinned. "But who is ever going to believe us?"

"Okay, that does it." Molly slapped the ground. "This is good luck, and I'm going to think *lucky* from now on!"

"Me, too!" declared Max. Then he saw a strange expression creep over Molly's face as she picked up her hand and looked at it. "What's wrong?" She held her hand out for him to see. Clinging to her damp palm were several bright orange hairs.

CHAPTER SIX

Not far away in an air sac, a great white blood cell muttered to herself. "My work is never done!" She slithered along into another air sac and looked around. "Tsk, tsk, look at this mess. What *am* I to do?" She made herself a new arm, snatched up something from the ground, and gobbled it down with greedy little gulps. "More dust!" she flapped little arms in the air, "and dirt and smoke! What can this Body be doing?" She scoured ahead, paddling with fat little arms, picking up as she went. Nibbling and clucking disapproval, she left behind a spotless pink wake. "Bless me, now what?" She stopped short and stared.

Something told Baxter it was time to wake up. He stretched languidly on his curved, soft bed, flicked an ear, and opened his eyes to gaze dreamily at the peaceful mist.

Their eyes met.

Baxter leaped up, arched his back, and hissed. He sidled away against a wall. The cell reared up and rushed forward. "Invader!" she bellowed, waving blob arms. "Lunch!"

The roar split the fog, ringing with echoes that reached Max and Molly from several directions. "Baxter!" they yelled, and leaped up. They ran, stopped, spun around, and ran in another direction, unable to tell sound from echo and not knowing which way to go.

Baxter spit and struck the air with his claws. The cell roared again, opening a mouth wide enough to swallow several cats his size.

"NO!" shrieked Molly. She burst through the mist and snatched Baxter up in her arms. Max jumped between them and the great cell, yelling and waving. The cell roared again and stretched her mouth even wider—lunch would have three courses today.

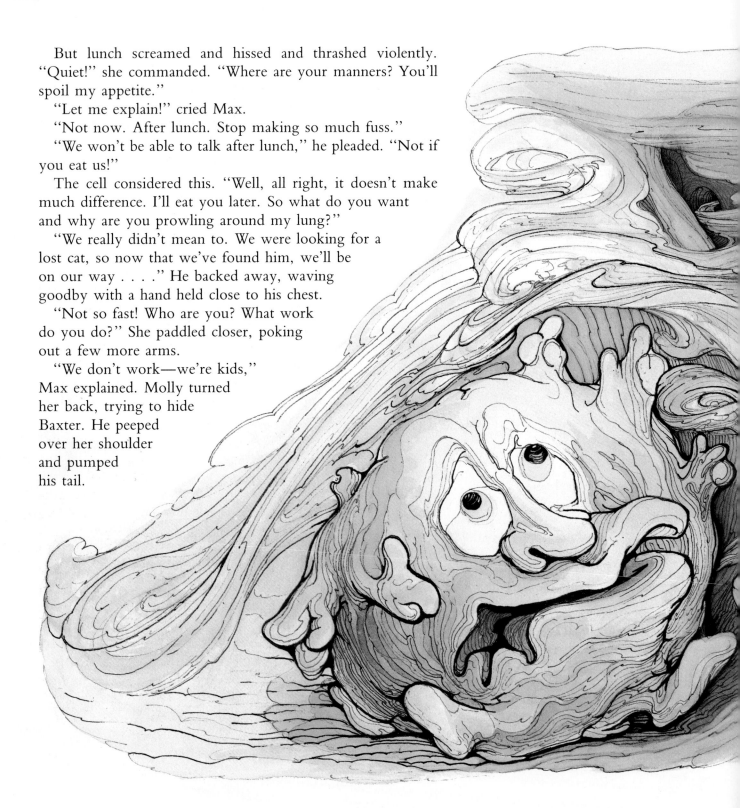

But lunch screamed and hissed and thrashed violently. "Quiet!" she commanded. "Where are your manners? You'll spoil my appetite."

"Let me explain!" cried Max.

"Not now. After lunch. Stop making so much fuss."

"We won't be able to talk after lunch," he pleaded. "Not if you eat us!"

The cell considered this. "Well, all right, it doesn't make much difference. I'll eat you later. So what do you want and why are you prowling around my lung?"

"We really didn't mean to. We were looking for a lost cat, so now that we've found him, we'll be on our way . . . ." He backed away, waving goodby with a hand held close to his chest.

"Not so fast! Who are you? What work do you do?" She paddled closer, poking out a few more arms.

"We don't work—we're kids," Max explained. Molly turned her back, trying to hide Baxter. He peeped over her shoulder and pumped his tail.

Max talked fast, trying to distract the cell as Molly edged away. "We're little humans." The magic word worked.

"Humans?" she gaped in dismay. "What have you done with your other arms and legs?"

"We live in the outside world, and this is all we need," said Max. "Really, they're quite enough."

"Well, it's no wonder you don't work, poor things, you can't be much good." She plucked a speck of dirt, nibbled it thoughtfully, and licked her fingers. Then she leaned over, studied him closely, and said, "You must be from Upstairs. I've asked and asked for someone to come down and talk to me. It's about time you showed up. You won't find a harder working macrophage than me. I do my job. But with all this *filth* pouring down"—she flapped her arms, causing several fluffy specks to scurry away—"how's a body to cope?"

"Did you say you're a macrophage?" asked Max.

"That's right, be sure to get it right in your report. I'm a white blood cell of the defense system, assigned to the lung. I have the most important job: cleaning it up so oxygen can pass through into the capillaries. I love my work, but I'm beginning to get upset. Tell them that," she sniffed, "Upstairs!"

"We will." Max nodded energetically, edging for the door.

"We need communication . . . cooperation . . ." They backed through the door, smiling and nodding, leaving the cell flailing the air. "Dust! Dirt! Fuzz! Fur! And that nasty little orange beast! Hey!" she yelled. "That was different. That was no Human! That was AN ALIEN!" She roared in pursuit through the door and found . . . an empty room. "Where did they go?" She rushed around it, searching, but all she found was a tuft of orange fur, stuck in the wall between two flat cells. Yanking it out, she gnashed at it furiously. "What is this lung coming to?" she muttered. Then she waddled away, leaving behind her a clean pink trail, like the path of a vacuum cleaner, dust-free.

The escapees huddled together in a capillary just behind the wall. Molly hugged Baxter. He scowled and switched his tail. "Poor fellow, we had to bring you here." She stroked his sopping wet fur. "We had to get away."

"Nice going, Max, that was pretty creative," she said, disengaging a claw from her shoulder.

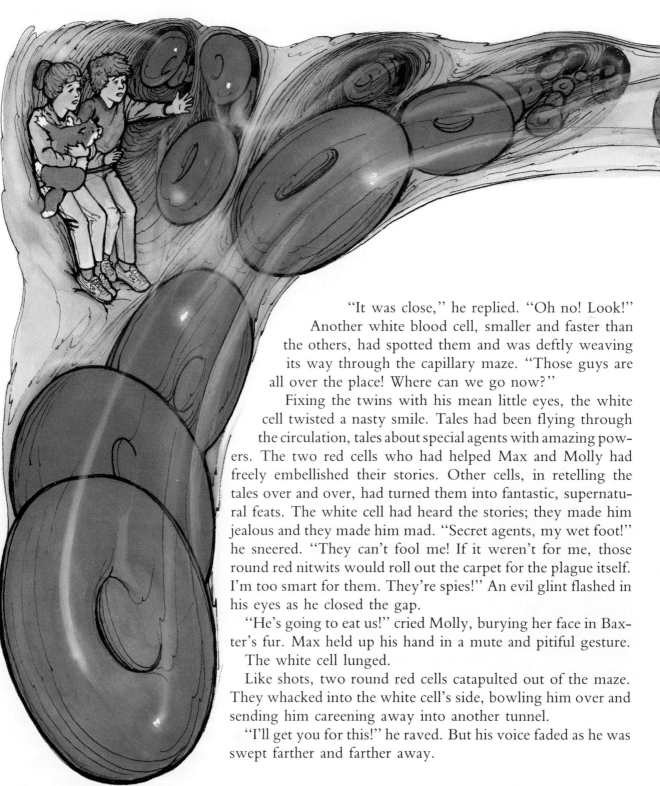

"It was close," he replied. "Oh no! Look!" Another white blood cell, smaller and faster than the others, had spotted them and was deftly weaving its way through the capillary maze. "Those guys are all over the place! Where can we go now?"

Fixing the twins with his mean little eyes, the white cell twisted a nasty smile. Tales had been flying through the circulation, tales about special agents with amazing powers. The two red cells who had helped Max and Molly had freely embellished their stories. Other cells, in retelling the tales over and over, had turned them into fantastic, supernatural feats. The white cell had heard the stories; they made him jealous and they made him mad. "Secret agents, my wet foot!" he sneered. "They can't fool me! If it weren't for me, those round red nitwits would roll out the carpet for the plague itself. I'm too smart for them. They're spies!" An evil glint flashed in his eyes as he closed the gap.

"He's going to eat us!" cried Molly, burying her face in Baxter's fur. Max held up his hand in a mute and pitiful gesture.

The white cell lunged.

Like shots, two round red cells catapulted out of the maze. They whacked into the white cell's side, bowling him over and sending him careening away into another tunnel.

"I'll get you for this!" he raved. But his voice faded as he was swept farther and farther away.

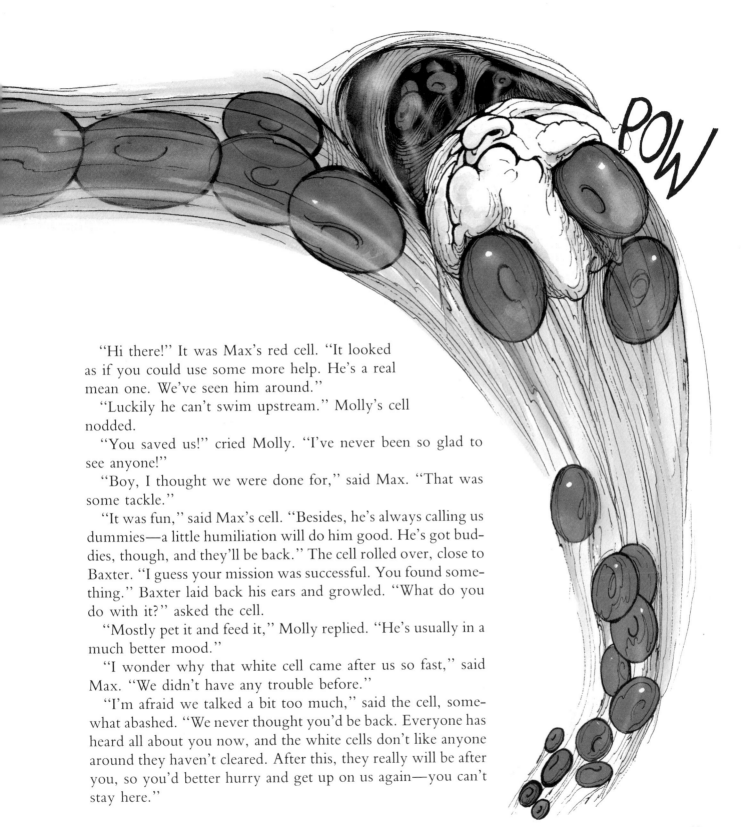

"Hi there!" It was Max's red cell. "It looked as if you could use some more help. He's a real mean one. We've seen him around."

"Luckily he can't swim upstream." Molly's cell nodded.

"You saved us!" cried Molly. "I've never been so glad to see anyone!"

"Boy, I thought we were done for," said Max. "That was some tackle."

"It was fun," said Max's cell. "Besides, he's always calling us dummies—a little humiliation will do him good. He's got buddies, though, and they'll be back." The cell rolled over, close to Baxter. "I guess your mission was successful. You found something." Baxter laid back his ears and growled. "What do you do with it?" asked the cell.

"Mostly pet it and feed it," Molly replied. "He's usually in a much better mood."

"I wonder why that white cell came after us so fast," said Max. "We didn't have any trouble before."

"I'm afraid we talked a bit too much," said the cell, somewhat abashed. "We never thought you'd be back. Everyone has heard all about you now, and the white cells don't like anyone around they haven't cleared. After this, they really will be after you, so you'd better hurry and get up on us again—you can't stay here."

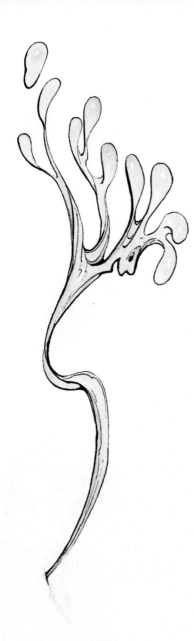

"We'll have to take you back through the heart, but we'll drop you off the first chance we get," said the other cell. "But from now on, you'd better stay out of the blood."

"Think lucky, thinklucky, thinkluckythinklucky . . ." Molly chanted to herself, lifting Baxter up onto the cell. He grabbed and stuck. She hoisted herself up behind, waved to Max, and they floated away.

"HI GANG!" Freewilly slipped through the capillary wall, thin as a string, and re-formed. "I see you found the cat. See, no trouble at all. I don't mind if I say I told you so."

"*I* mind, so don't," said Max, but Freewilly, oblivious, cheered and prated until he was drowned out by the rumbling of the heart.

They rushed into the left atrium and through the bicuspid valve into the gigantic left ventricle. Its gnarled walls convulsed with monumental force and spurted them into a huge vessel. Another valve clacked shut behind them.

"Aorta!" screamed Freewilly when he had collected himself. The aorta stretched and heaved and shot them into one of its many branches.

"This is an artery on the way to the head," Molly's red cell told them.

Freewilly quickly added, "Arteries go away from the heart toward the cells. The blood is under great pressure, so that arteries must have strong, muscular walls to keep from bursting."

They heard booms behind them and after each one felt a surge of power that drove them along. "It's the pulse!" Max exclaimed. They twisted and turned and began to slow down.

"Here come the capillaries!" called Freewilly as the vessels branched smaller and smaller. "Shall we go around again?"

"We don't dare," said Max. "They're looking for us. We have to get out of the blood."

"Foof! They won't bother you if I'm with you."

Max and Molly exchanged glances and dismounted at once. They waved goodby to their red cells, now noticeably darker, since they had given oxygen to the cells beyond the capillary walls.

"All right, if you insist." Freewilly shrugged. "But it's not going to be easy."

"Why?" asked Molly.

"Because this is the brain. It's our master computer. Security is tight. If you don't believe me, try to make a hole in this wall."

The twins each grasped an edge of two adjoining cells. "We already did this in the lung," said Max. But this time the cells resisted.

"Hey, what are you trying to do?" one cell asked. "We can't have you going in there. The brain is a delicate mechanism, and our job is to screen everything that goes through."

"Let go of my edge!" demanded the other.

"It's quite all right." Freewilly put on an official air. "They are with me, and I have clearance. My fluids carry the food and oxygen to the cells in there." The two flat cells conferred as Freewilly turned to the twins. "You will be welcome if you are with me. I'm very well known here. The brain cells are marvelously intelligent and love conversation. I find them quite up to my standards."

The two capillary cells were still doubtful but finally agreed after Freewilly gave extravagant guarantees.

"Now put some muscle on that crack," he directed, "and let's get going."

This time the capillary cells gave way and allowed them to pry open a small hole barely big enough to squeeze through.

"I'll go. Then you push Baxter through and I'll catch him," said Max, and disappeared head first. Molly gave Baxter a shove and squeezed in behind him. Freewilly stretched out, flipped, and followed. The hole snapped shut, and security was restored.

CHAPTER SEVEN

There's nothing here!" yelled Max. The three of them
had popped through the hole and were falling in a cool, cloudy
haze. Around them fine wires threaded in all directions in tan-
gles and festoons, as if some fantastic cobweb had been woven
through the brain to catch thoughts. Eerie lights appeared suddenly, sped along the wires, and vanished in pale-gray clouds.
"Quick!" yelled Max. "Grab this!" They caught one of the
wires. It was thin, slick, and tilted down. They slipped along it
until they crashed into something large and soft.

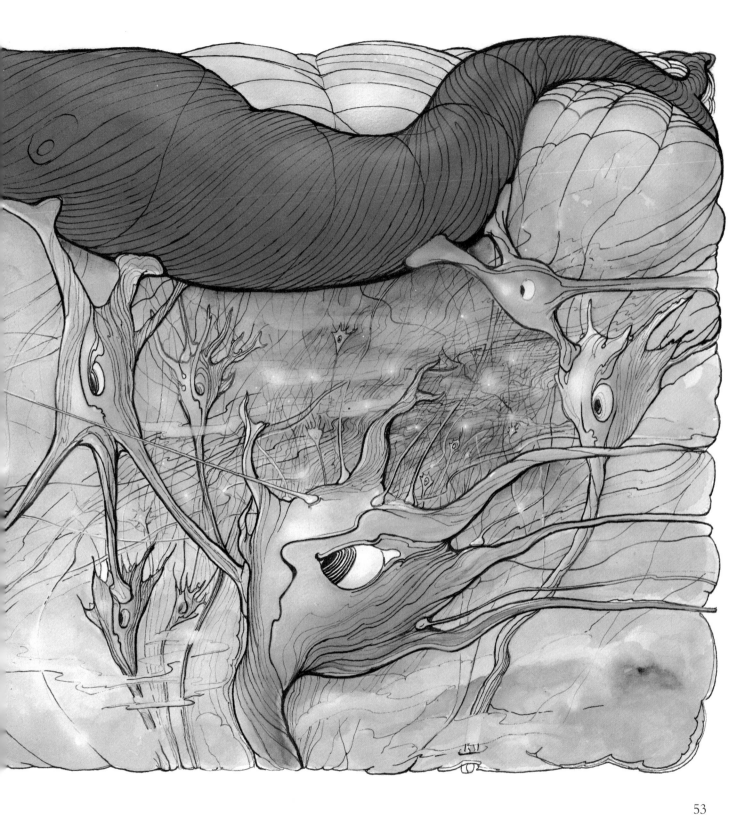

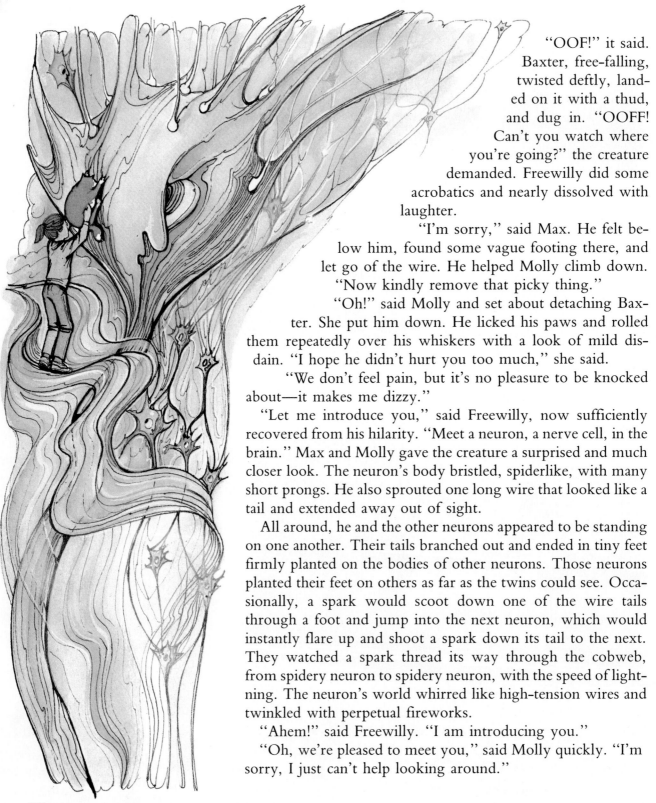

"OOF!" it said. Baxter, free-falling, twisted deftly, landed on it with a thud, and dug in. "OOFF! Can't you watch where you're going?" the creature demanded. Freewilly did some acrobatics and nearly dissolved with laughter.

"I'm sorry," said Max. He felt below him, found some vague footing there, and let go of the wire. He helped Molly climb down. "Now kindly remove that picky thing."

"Oh!" said Molly and set about detaching Baxter. She put him down. He licked his paws and rolled them repeatedly over his whiskers with a look of mild disdain. "I hope he didn't hurt you too much," she said.

"We don't feel pain, but it's no pleasure to be knocked about—it makes me dizzy."

"Let me introduce you," said Freewilly, now sufficiently recovered from his hilarity. "Meet a neuron, a nerve cell, in the brain." Max and Molly gave the creature a surprised and much closer look. The neuron's body bristled, spiderlike, with many short prongs. He also sprouted one long wire that looked like a tail and extended away out of sight.

All around, he and the other neurons appeared to be standing on one another. Their tails branched out and ended in tiny feet firmly planted on the bodies of other neurons. Those neurons planted their feet on others as far as the twins could see. Occasionally, a spark would scoot down one of the wire tails through a foot and jump into the next neuron, which would instantly flare up and shoot a spark down its tail to the next. They watched a spark thread its way through the cobweb, from spidery neuron to spidery neuron, with the speed of lightning. The neuron's world whirred like high-tension wires and twinkled with perpetual fireworks.

"Ahem!" said Freewilly. "I am introducing you."

"Oh, we're pleased to meet you," said Molly quickly. "I'm sorry, I just can't help looking around."

"They thought they'd drop in for a visit," said Freewilly. "Get it? 'Drop in'?" He broke up with laughter again.

"We get it, Freewilly," said Max. 'Thanks again for warning us." Then he added, "You really love it when we get into trouble, don't you?"

"Oh yes, that's the best part!" Freewilly agreed.

"Wow!" exclaimed Molly, looking around again. "It's like the Fourth of July."

"That's how we communicate," said the neuron. "Communication is my job. See, these are my dendrites"—he wiggled his many short prongs—"and this is my axon." He waggled his long wire tail. "Other neurons send me electrical messages along their axons to their nerve endings"—he indicated the tiny feet standing all over him—"where the messages jump across tiny spaces, called synapses, into me. Then I transmit the messages along my axon to my nerve endings at someone else's synapses. It goes on and on from there."

"How many times?" asked Molly.

"As many as it takes to get where it's going. There are millions of us, and each one is connected in relays to thousands of others. We are communications experts."

"You'd have to be," said Molly.

"I am sensory neuron #7622742637633, ipsilateral geniculate, visual relay, cone, blue, first intercept, right lateral fovea, quadrant 3, superfine. That about pins it down."

"What did he say?" asked Molly.

"Simple!" said Freewilly. "He receives blue from the right eye and sends it on. I could have told you that."

"I like to be exact," said the neuron. "Now that you know who I am, I'd like to know who you are and why you are dropping around loose."

Max figured it might be safer if he were not so exact, considering their previous encounters with strange new cells. He stalled. "We're ah, er, kids." He did not mention Baxter. The neuron eyed them and was about to speak, when suddenly and without warning, a spark dashed in and leaped across a synapse. In a split second, he flinched, flared brightly, and fired lightning down his tail. Molly shrieked, Max leaped back, and Baxter fled behind them.

"Are you all right?" asked the neuron.

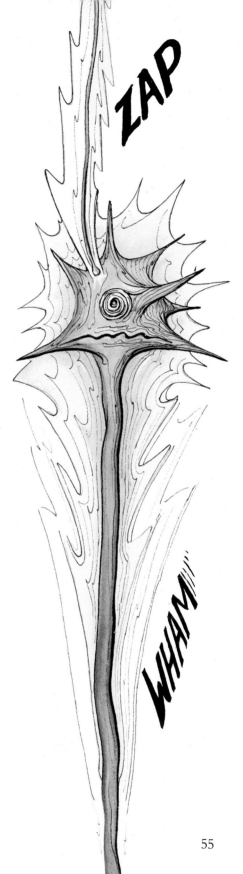

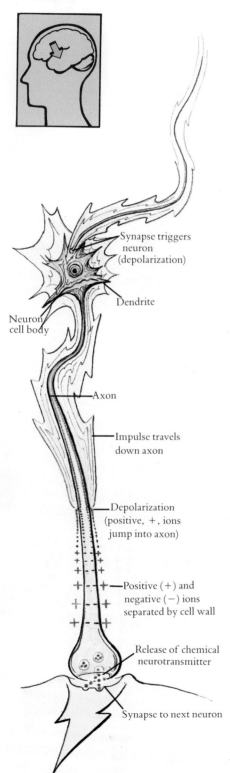

Synapse triggers neuron (depolarization)

Dendrite

Neuron cell body

Axon

Impulse travels down axon

Depolarization (positive, +, ions jump into axon)

Positive (+) and negative (−) ions separated by cell wall

Release of chemical neurotransmitter

Synapse to next neuron

"Are *you* all right?" cried Max. "I thought you had been electrocuted!" Freewilly hopped up and down, clapping and laughing. He shed so much water he had to scramble about to gather it back before he could carry on.

"Oh no, we love electricity," replied the neuron, watching Freewilly. "I fail to see what's so funny, little fellow."

Freewilly froze. Then he sucked up several drops more than he really needed, flitted up to the neuron with his hands on his hips, and glared. "Little fellow? FOOF! You overheated spark plug. I'll tell you what's so funny. I was thinking how crispy you'd be if you did get electrocuted." Then he turned toward the twins with an air of authority. "Neurons can only generate enough electricity to tickle each other." Triumphant, he turned his back on the neuron and floated a little way off.

"Tickle!" the neuron bristled. "It was enough to depolarize me!"

"Foof." Freewilly tossed over his shoulder.

"Depolarize?" asked Molly. "Did it hurt?"

"Not at all, we're built for it. Let me explain," the neuron went on coolly, ignoring Freewilly. "I work with electric charges. Since they are also chemical, we call them ions."

"I know about them," said Max. "Negative and positive ions are always trying to get together—it's called attraction."

"That's for sure! When I'm in my resting state, like now, I carefully separate negative from positive and push positive ions outside my axon. They keep trying to get back inside, so I have to hold them out. But when I get depolarized by a spark, I turn them all loose and WHAM! They leap back inside and depolarize me all the way down to my toes!" He wiggled his axon. "It feels so good!"

Molly tried very hard to understand. "Batteries have negative and positive ends, is that the same?"

"They're called poles," said Max. "Remember when we wired them together, we got a spark?"

"Well, these guys are all wired in a row," Molly replied.

"And the synapses are like switches between them," Max added.

"That's how we send our messages," the neuron concluded. "We depolarize."

"What did that message say?" asked Molly. "Did you have

time to read it?"

"I don't need to, they all say the same thing. The eye saw bright blue. I relayed it to Visual Perception, and they'll relay it to Thinking. Thinking will decide what to do about it. They might notify Motor Acting to move some part of the Body. But I never find out what goes on at that end."

"How far are you from Thinking?" asked Max.

"A long, long way!" Freewilly declared. The neuron took no notice.

"Thinking is up in the cortex, the top dome of the brain. Up there, they have departments for Vision, Hearing, Learning, Language, Memory, and Imagination. Unconscious Activity is in the base of the brain."

"Unconscious Activity? How can it be active if it's unconscious?" asked Molly.

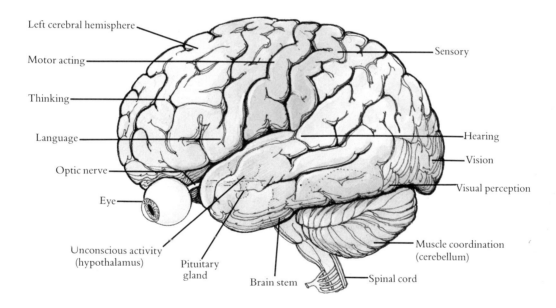

"That's the automatic behaviors, such as digestion, heartbeat, breathing, and growing."

"The brain controls growing?" Max asked eagerly. "Can it think the Body into growing up taller?'

"Or quicker?" asked Molly with equal enthusiasm.

"Certainly not! Thinking can change many things, but not growing."

"Why not?" Max insisted. "You just said it does."

"I said Unconscious Activity does, and nobody tells them what to do." The neuron eyed them again. "Why are you so interested, anyway?"

"Tell him," whispered Molly. "He's been really nice. He might be able to help us."

"I guess we should explain. We don't belong here," Max confessed. "We're lost." He told the whole story. The neuron listened carefully, occasionally asking him to explain or repeat certain parts. When Max was finished, he responded.

"I knew there was something strange about you two. You're not regular types around here. You're too curious to be cells—they're never interested in anyone but themselves, neurons excepted, of course. And you're much too pleasant to be like Freewilly."

"We're little humans," Molly added.

"You know, I figured that. I don't know how, either—I'm not in Perceiving. Now I know why you're so interested in growing up. You Humans do that, don't you?"

"We're trying," said Molly, "but it's not easy."

"Well, take my advice and don't waste your time thinking about it. It won't do you any good. Just leave Unconscious Activity alone. Believe me, you won't regret it."

"What do you mean?" asked Max.

"How would you like to have to think about breathing, just for example? You would have to think 'inhale' and notify all the right muscles. Then you would have to think 'exhale' and wait, think 'inhale' and 'exhale' all day every day. Suppose you wanted to run. You'd need to breathe faster and make your heart beat faster so the muscle cells could cook up the energy."

"Not to mention telling the legs to move," said Max.

"We wouldn't have time for anything else!" said Molly. "We wouldn't dare go to sleep, and we'd be tired all the time just from staying alive. That wouldn't be much fun. I guess I can wait to grow up."

"You're catching on," said the neuron. "Unconscious Activity will do a better job anyway. They will coordinate all the cells so that the bones, muscles, nerves, and blood vessels all grow up together."

"I sure couldn't remember all that," said Molly. "I have

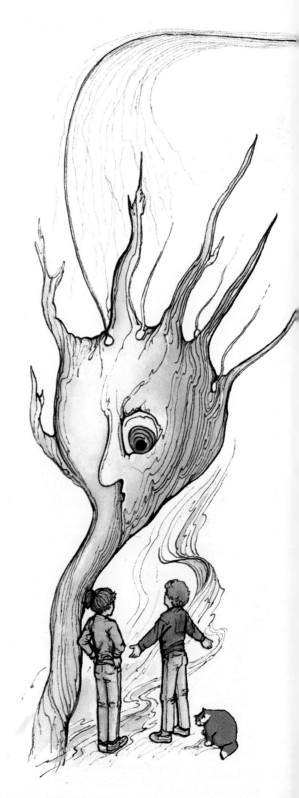

trouble remembering what day it is—especially during vacation."

"Well, we insist on that perfect memory. We insist on perfect coordination everywhere," the neuron declared. "All cells live in harmony and mutual benefit. Each cell does its job, never making mistakes, never doing anything wrong. It's a perfect world—nobody but Freewilly ever gets out of line."

Freewilly had floated much closer and heard. "How about some big hot-heads!" But nobody paid attention. Molly was wondering if all that good-natured harmony might not be awfully boring. Fighting with Max kept her sharp, she thought, even though nobody won. Max was analyzing.

"The Body is like a country," he said, with a faraway look in his eye. "The blood vessels are the highways between the organs—the cities. The organ-cities that work together make a system, or state. The stomach and intestines are organs that belong to the same system-state. The heart and blood belong to another, and the muscles and bones to another. Neurons are the telephones. Billions of cells are the citizens who work in the factories inside the organ-cities and the system-states. And the brain is the government . . ."

"Max!" exclaimed Molly. "There you go again. I thought we agreed to concentrate on how to get out of here. You can analyze all you want after that."

"Sorry," Max replied sheepishly. "I forgot. But it was pretty good, don't you think?"

"Wonderful." Molly turned to the neuron. "We really have to get out of this Body and go home. It's not that we don't think it's fascinating and perfect like you say it is. I'm sure it is. But we belong somewhere else. Would you help us? Do you know any way out?"

"I wish I did, but I'm only in Visual. I don't know anything about Out There. What about Freewilly? He gets around."

"He insists nobody gets out—or even wants to," said Max.

"Hmmm," said the neuron. "What's out there now?"

"We don't know," said Max.

"Why don't you go look?"

"How?"

"Out through the eye."

"Wow," said Max. "Maybe if we could see out we would know what the Body is doing and could figure out how we got swallowed."

"And maybe reverse it and get out!" said Molly. "What a great idea!"

"Well, maybe not great, but it was good, wasn't it?" the neuron replied. "And to think that Ideas aren't my department—I just dabble."

"How can we get to an eye?" asked Molly.

"Just follow the axon that depolarized me. It comes from an eye." He waggled his dendrites to wave goodby. They marched away. Baxter trotted ahead. Freewilly soon drifted up, muttering.

"Are you sure we can find it?" asked Molly. "There's hundreds of axons and they all look alike."

"I know the way," said Freewilly. "I never get lost. Besides"—he flung his arms in a spacious gesture toward a giant cable—"all these axons come from there. That's the optic nerve, coming from the eye."

"Just the same, I think I'll trace this one," said Molly.

Freewilly was soon bubbling with enthusiasm. "I can hardly wait! Oh, I love the eye! And you'll love it too, I know you will."

"I hope you behave," said Max. "You haven't been doing too well up to now."

"Hey, don't look at me. It wasn't me who tangled with white blood cells. Nobody fights them and wins."

"What do you mean, fight? We ran for our lives," declared Molly. She prodded Baxter with her toe. He had stopped to poke at something no one else could see.

"Besides," said Max, "You keep talking about how wonderful and perfect and orderly the Body is. How come you pick on each other?"

"It was orderly before you got here." Freewilly sniffed, floating ahead with his nose in the air.

"There's the eyeball!" exclaimed Molly, mostly to change the subject, for it was still a long way off. "It's enormous!" They traced the axon and followed Freewilly along the long optic nerve as it passed through the back wall of the glistening white globe and emerged into a luminous cathedral of light.

Streaming at them through a circle above, light flickered and shifted in a glowing funnel that crossed the space of the eye, flooding its whole inner surface with one gigantic dancing pattern of brightness.

61

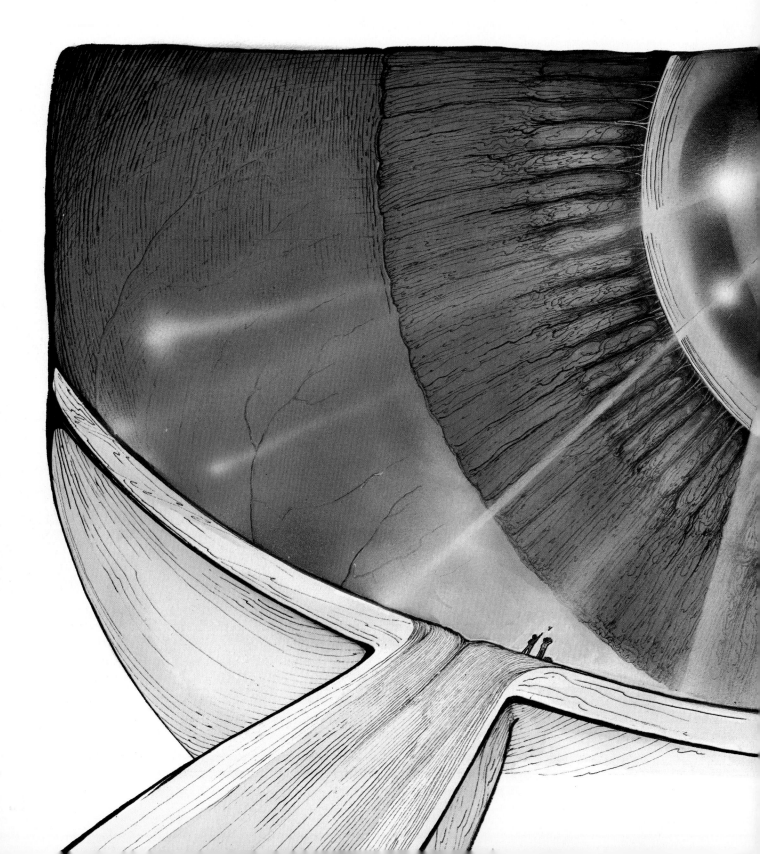

CHAPTER EIGHT

"Look, a full moon!" exclaimed Molly.

"Moon!" cried Freewilly. "Don't be stupid. That's the lens, and the light is coming through it from Out There."

"I know," Molly replied. "I only meant it looks like a full moon. It's just a surprise to see light coming *in* through the pupil. My pupils seem black since I usually see them from the outside, see?" She spread her eyelids with her fingers and leaned over toward him.

Freewilly peered at her eye. "That's not black, that's blue," he declared.

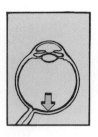

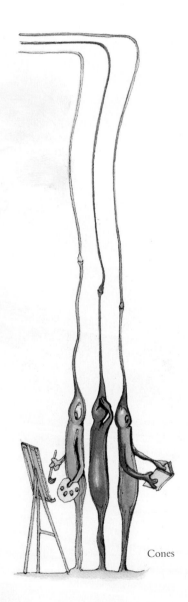

Cones

"No, no, you're looking at my iris, the ring around the pupil. It's in the middle of that, and it's black."

"Imagine that," Freewilly said. "How odd. Your iris is terribly wrinkled, isn't it?"

Max was looking at the iris from inside. "Look, you can see it there behind the lens. The pupil is the hole that's bright, and the iris is practically black. It's just backward."

The inner surface of the eye was lined most of the way around with a smooth orange carpet. Blood vessels forked and spread from the spot where they stood and fanned over its surface. The thousands of axons fanned out under the vessels and spread evenly through the carpet. Baxter crouched, thrashed his tail, and watched the patterns of light on its surface. He stalked and pounced on a flicker. He lifted his paw to look under. There was nothing there. The flicker danced on the back of his head.

"Make him behave," said Freewilly. "This is no place for such foolishness."

"You explain that to Baxter," laughed Max. Baxter soon tired of his fruitless hunt and rolled himself up for a nap.

Molly was still tracing her axon. It led her across the eye, then suddenly dived into the surface. "Look, this carpet is full of millions of pop bottles all crammed together, standing on their ends."

"That's not a carpet, it's the retina!" Freewilly corrected her. "And those are the light-sensing cells, the rods and cones." He floated to her and pointed a water-drop finger down. "This is the fovea, the spot directly across from the center of the lens."

"It looks different here."

"That's because only cones live here. It's the very best spot, the cultural center. Cones in the fovea are responsible for the finest, clearest vision in the eye."

"Then I must use my foveas when I read. I can see best when I look right at something," Max said.

"That's your cones at work, and you'd better give them plenty of light. They insist on lots of light before they will respond." Freewilly flourished and bowed low as if to introduce them. "I do wish you could meet them up close, but all these axons are cluttering up the space between us. Only I can go in there. Only I am invited. It's the best address in the eye.

Please don't stand so close—you're casting a shadow."

"Oops, sorry." Molly backed away and waved down at them. "They must be smart if they do all the reading."

"Quite so. They are cultured and artistic. Each cone can distinguish and signal red, blue, or green. Together they paint a picture in all the colors of the rainbow."

"How do they make white?" asked Max.

"They all signal at once; white is all colors together."

"Then how do they signal black?"

"Nobody signals; black is no light," Freewilly went on. "Cones are serious and sober, retire early, and never stay up after dark. They need time for rest and contemplation."

Max considered explaining to Freewilly about electric lights, but decided not to try.

"Now I know why I can't see colors so well in poor light," said Molly. "My cones are asleep."

"The cones will never accept anything poor! They are aristocrats and very discriminating. Nothing but the finest for them, especially those in the fovea. Why, each cone has its own private line directly to the brain. That way they give the brain the most refined and detailed image possible. Neuron number 7622742637633 received from here—blue, I believe."

"Right. I followed the axon and it came from here," Molly replied.

Freewilly waved at the cells in the fovea. "They look asleep, don't they? Oh, well, they're very fine folks, believe me! But"— he tossed a watery gesture toward the far edge of the retina— "it's not so with the rods, over there. They are crude and rowdy and have no talent whatsoever. Why, rods think the whole world is dark gray!" He confided in a lower voice, "They have bad manners, too. When they get stimulated, and it doesn't take much, they all yell at the brain on party lines. The picture they send is always rough and splotchy, with no fine detail, technique, or skill."

"They sound just like the fast film I get for my camera," said Max. "It doesn't need much light, but the pictures look grainy."

"'Fast' is the word for rods." Freewilly put his nose in the air. "Quite frankly, they aren't my type. I much prefer cones— they appeal to my sensitive, artistic nature."

Rods

"Egad." Molly marched off.

"Where are you going?" Freewilly demanded.

"To see the rods." The retina curved up, so she couldn't go far, but the farther she got from the fovea, the fewer cones she saw. Rods abounded. "If they're who's up at night, they must be the ones who help me see in the dark."

Max followed slowly, kicking flickers with his toes and wishing he could see the image on the retina. But it was too faint, and he was standing on it. Freewilly bustled after them, calling at Molly.

"You can't see in the dark. That's not possible. But if there's any light at all, the rods will find it and make a fuss over it. They're always looking for some excuse to holler, but bright light and study bore them and put them out. They sleep all day and wake up at night, all rested and ready to party." He concluded with a significant glance, "You can see why *they* don't belong in the fovea."

"Freewilly, you're an awful snob," said Max, poking Baxter with a toe. Baxter opened one eye, twitched his tail contentedly, and went back to sleep. "Anyhow, my rods aren't that rowdy. They don't seem to wake up so fast, either. When I go into a dark theater on a sunny day, it's a long time before I can see."

"Same here," said Molly, "and by then we've stumbled and spilled the popcorn."

"Rods are slow and lazy risers," Freewilly explained. "They have to pump themselves up with vitamin A before they can get going."

"I guess we should eat a carrot instead of the popcorn," Molly laughed.

"If the rods and cones are such opposites, how do they get along? You'd think they would argue all the time," said Max.

"Separate shifts," said Freewilly. "Besides, the retina is too well organized to let temperamental differences become a problem. The cells must discuss their work with one another, and they do so in perfect harmony."

Molly eyed him. "You just said they signal the brain, now you say they talk to each other."

"They do. Other neurons lie sideways on top of the rods and

cones and specialize in all sorts of cross-references. Why, some can even detect the movement of an image crossing the retina. They help the brain lock the eyes on the object and track it wherever it goes, even if it has to roll the eyes or move the head."

"I do that when I play a video game," exclaimed Max. "Hunters do it too!"

"Do you track and hunt video game?" asked Freewilly. "Do you eat them too?"

Molly giggled. "You might say he does. He devours them with his eyes." Freewilly looked momentarily puzzled, but nothing distracted him long from his lecturing.

"The retina has another superb trick," he went on. "If it decides too much light is overwhelming the neurons, it simply shuts some of them off. Then the rest of them can manage the picture."

"That's not so," Molly declared. "The iris does that. It pinches down and makes the pupil smaller to cut down on the light coming in. We had it in school!"

Freewilly shrugged. "Oh, that's true of course, but the retina does it better."

"You can't win around here!" Molly sighed.

"Hey, I thought of a great analogy!" exclaimed Max. "Listen to this!"

Molly sighed again. "I can hard-ly wait to see if you can top that Body-as-country one."

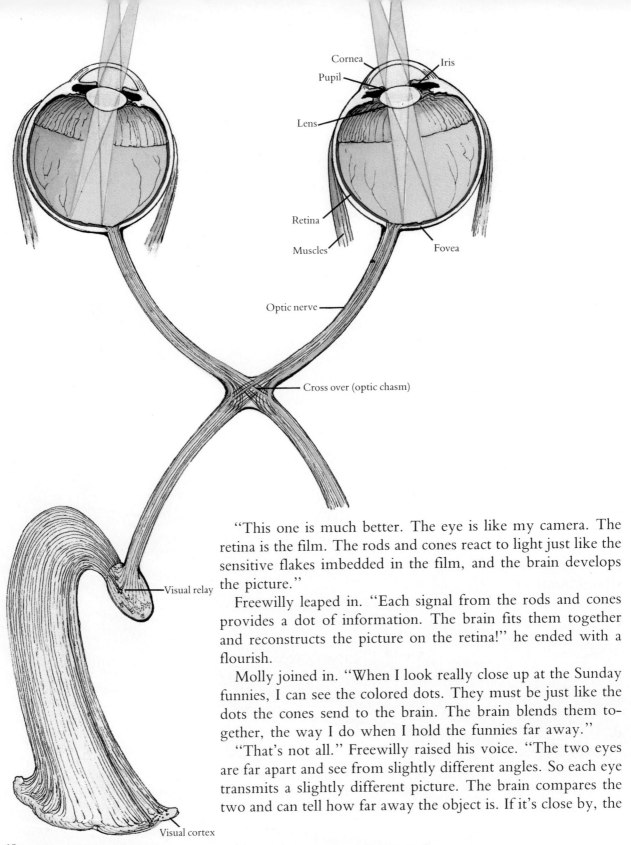

Cornea

Iris

Pupil

Lens

Retina

Muscles

Fovea

Optic nerve

Cross over (optic chasm)

Visual relay

Visual cortex

"This one is much better. The eye is like my camera. The retina is the film. The rods and cones react to light just like the sensitive flakes imbedded in the film, and the brain develops the picture."

Freewilly leaped in. "Each signal from the rods and cones provides a dot of information. The brain fits them together and reconstructs the picture on the retina!" he ended with a flourish.

Molly joined in. "When I look really close up at the Sunday funnies, I can see the colored dots. They must be just like the dots the cones send to the brain. The brain blends them together, the way I do when I hold the funnies far away."

"That's not all." Freewilly raised his voice. "The two eyes are far apart and see from slightly different angles. So each eye transmits a slightly different picture. The brain compares the two and can tell how far away the object is. If it's close by, the two pictures are *real* different, see?" He thrust a long wet finger at Molly's nose. "The brain molds the pictures together and makes 3-D." He drove his finger onto the tip of her nose.

"Stop that!" She jerked her head back and caught sight of something moving overhead. "Hey! The lens is wobbling. It's going to fall!"

Freewilly laughed so hard he sprinkled. "It's adjusting, silly. It's focusing on something Out There, something that's close by." Then he assumed his lecturing attitude and carried on. "Light rays need to be bent so they will focus a clear picture on the retina. Focusing is the job of the lens. It bends light with its curvature. Something far away needs a thin, flat lens, but something close by needs one that's round and fat. There's a circle of muscles around the lens holding it by tiny strings, and when they pull, the lens fattens up. Close-up objects are more work for the muscles because they need a fatter lens. That's what you saw."

"It must be those little muscles that get tired when I read a lot," said Max. "We're supposed to look at the horizon to rest them. But let's go back to my analogy. If the eye is like a camera, then the picture on the retina would be upside down and backward. I looked at the ground glass in the back of a camera once, and that's what I saw. Lenses do that. They bend the light so much the beams crisscross and flop the picture. The brain must have to turn it back around!"

"How would it know to do that?" asked Molly. Then she looked at her hands. "Unless my fingers told my brain what was rightside up."

"The brain gets information from everywhere," said Freewilly, peering up at the pupil window. "Funny, I never thought about ups and downs Out There. Amazing."

"The *brain* is amazing!" said Molly. "It aims the eyes, focuses the lenses, compares the pictures, blends the colors, and turns it over to boot!"

"Then," Max added, "it decides what it's seeing and what to do about it."

"And then does it!" said Molly, finally having the last word.

Suddenly they were drenched in blinding light. It blazed in through the pupil and lens. Cones shrieked in surprise. Rods yelled and tried to shut off.

"OW!" cried the twins as their eyes clamped shut. Baxter leaped up, waking in midair. All over the retina, cells were screaming and dispatching alarms, sending sparks shooting for the optic nerve.

"I have to see!" Molly thought, forcing her eyes to open. She looked up. The lens was wobbling and the iris was pinching down, but just for a second, she could see Out There. Dazed, she had to wait until the calamity had died down before she could whisper to Max, "Did you see that?"

"What? My eyes were shut."

"Out There. I looked out the eye and I saw . . . wood rafters."

"Rafters!"

"Yes, just like in Grandma's attic. I think this eye is looking up . . . at the attic roof."

"That's impossible! That would mean this Body was lying on the attic floor. That can't be. You made a mistake."

"I know what I saw. Don't tell me I didn't. It was the attic roof!"

"Where's Freewilly?"

"Right here. I got a bit scattered in all the excitement, but I'm all together now."

"Where is this Body, really?" demanded Max. "If you know, you'd better tell us. Now!" he pointed up at the pupil. "What is out there?"

Freewilly looked shocked. "Me? Where? Out There? How should I know? I'm an insider. That's not my department anymore. I resigned when they dragged me out of the sea. No. Someone else is in charge of that, not me."

"Max!" Molly stomped a foot. "It was the attic! We're on the floor right where—Oh my goodness! Right where we put that book."

Max stared at her. "The picture of the head with the open mouth!"

"And eyes."

"It can't be. How can we be in the book? You can't just go jump into a book."

"Unless it's a magic book."

"No! It has to make sense!"

"Why?" Molly shrugged. "Nothing else does."

"Hey," said Freewilly, offended. "Maybe your world doesn't make sense, but don't cast aspersions on mine! We are never lost, we always"—

"Oh stop it, or I'll cast your aspersions all over this eye!" Molly took a threatening step toward him.

"Don't!" He fled. "Come on, let's get out of here," he called. "That light might strike twice."

"Where's Baxter?"

"Here behind my legs. How do we get out?"

"The way we got in. Hurry up!"

"I'm coming as fast as I can."

They left the eye.

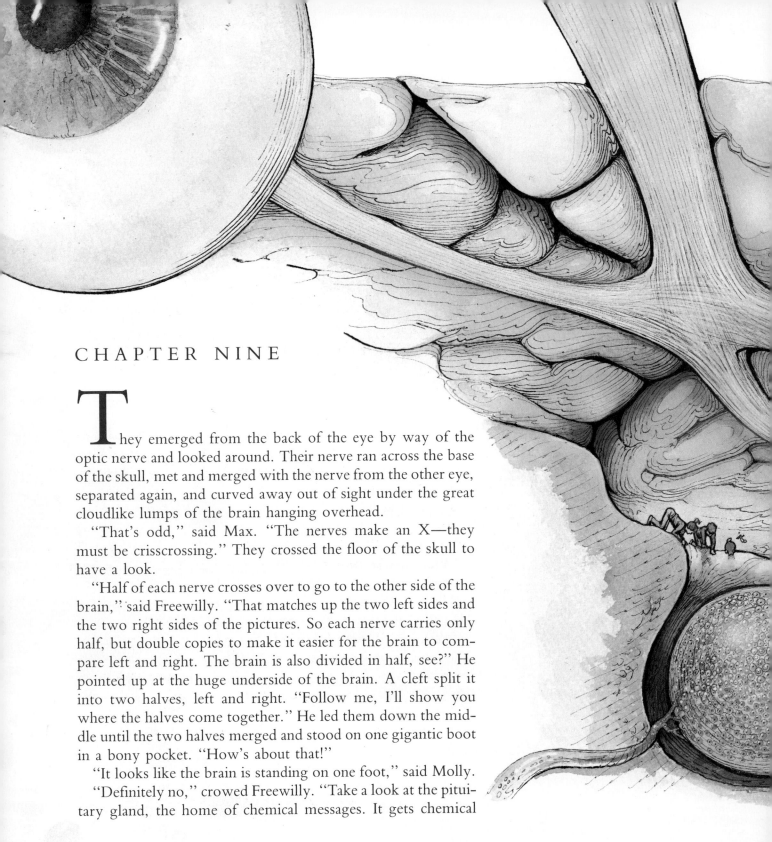

CHAPTER NINE

They emerged from the back of the eye by way of the optic nerve and looked around. Their nerve ran across the base of the skull, met and merged with the nerve from the other eye, separated again, and curved away out of sight under the great cloudlike lumps of the brain hanging overhead.

"That's odd," said Max. "The nerves make an X—they must be crisscrossing." They crossed the floor of the skull to have a look.

"Half of each nerve crosses over to go to the other side of the brain," said Freewilly. "That matches up the two left sides and the two right sides of the pictures. So each nerve carries only half, but double copies to make it easier for the brain to compare left and right. The brain is also divided in half, see?" He pointed up at the huge underside of the brain. A cleft split it into two halves, left and right. "Follow me, I'll show you where the halves come together." He led them down the middle until the two halves merged and stood on one gigantic boot in a bony pocket. "How's about that!"

"It looks like the brain is standing on one foot," said Molly.

"Definitely no," crowed Freewilly. "Take a look at the pituitary gland, the home of chemical messages. It gets chemical

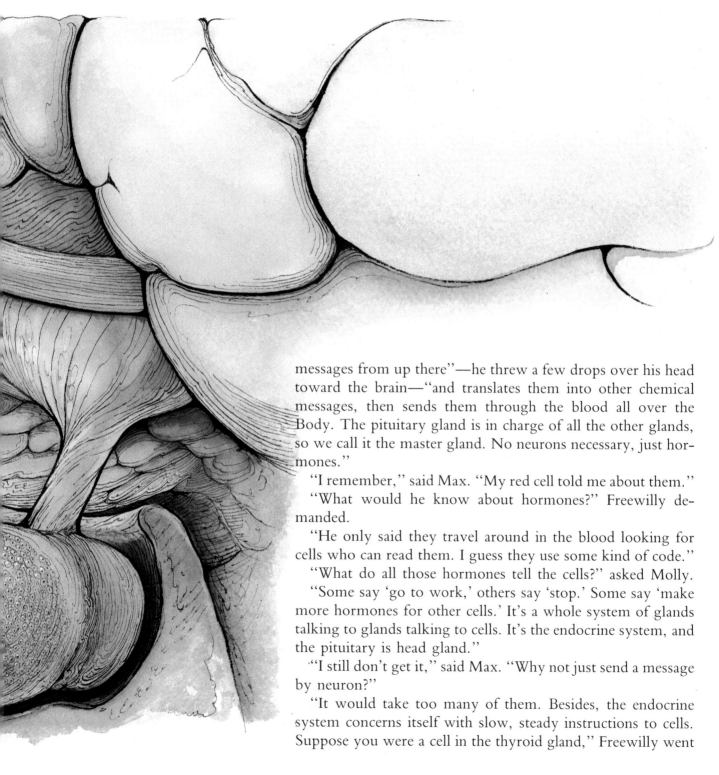

messages from up there"—he threw a few drops over his head toward the brain—"and translates them into other chemical messages, then sends them through the blood all over the Body. The pituitary gland is in charge of all the other glands, so we call it the master gland. No neurons necessary, just hormones."

"I remember," said Max. "My red cell told me about them."

"What would he know about hormones?" Freewilly demanded.

"He only said they travel around in the blood looking for cells who can read them. I guess they use some kind of code."

"What do all those hormones tell the cells?" asked Molly.

"Some say 'go to work,' others say 'stop.' Some say 'make more hormones for other cells.' It's a whole system of glands talking to glands talking to cells. It's the endocrine system, and the pituitary is head gland."

"'I still don't get it," said Max. "Why not just send a message by neuron?"

"It would take too many of them. Besides, the endocrine system concerns itself with slow, steady instructions to cells. Suppose you were a cell in the thyroid gland," Freewilly went on. "You get a message from the pituitary. It would tell you to make thyroid hormone, which would go out and tell the cells to eat more, increasing metabolism, as we call it. Suppose you were a cell in the pancreas. You'd make insulin, which would tell the cells to hurry up and suck more food through their walls."

"I thought you told us back in the intestine that the pancreas makes digestive juice," said Molly.

"It does, it's a double gland. Hormones control the kidneys and growing"—

"Growing!" Max peered at the pituitary. "Maybe we could get some of that hormone and make ourselves big again." Molly called and waved and knocked on its wall. None of the cells took the slightest notice. They chugged away, industriously pumping out minuscule bubbles of hormones and dumping them into capillaries.

"See?" said Freewilly. "They won't bother with you. I told you so!"

"Oh, well." Max sighed and turned away. "Let's get going."

Following Freewilly, they skirted the base of the skull, scrambled down a ridge, and found a hole in the bone. A great nerve emerged from the hole and rose up to the brain. Freewilly waved them toward the hole, coaxing them to hurry.

"I'm not so sure we should just follow him around," said Max. "He's trying to distract us and convince us to stay."

"He does a good job," said Molly. "This place is really incredible."

"Now don't you start!"

"I'm not. But I don't think it does any harm to explore. After all, we decided to learn as much as we can. Besides, how else will we ever find our way out?"

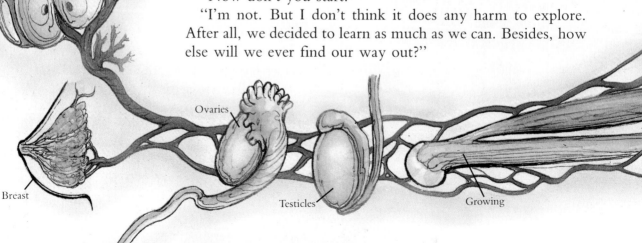

Cells

Breast

Ovaries

Testicles

Growing

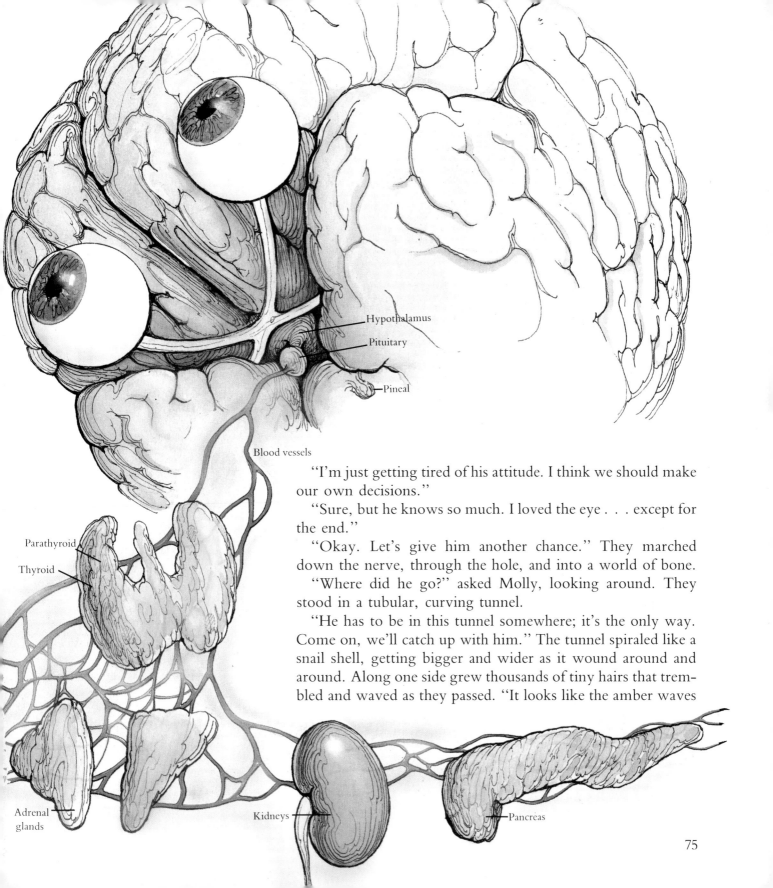

Hypothalamus

Pituitary

Pineal

Blood vessels

Parathyroid

Thyroid

Adrenal
glands

Kidneys

Pancreas

"I'm just getting tired of his attitude. I think we should make our own decisions."

"Sure, but he knows so much. I loved the eye . . . except for the end."

"Okay. Let's give him another chance." They marched down the nerve, through the hole, and into a world of bone.

"Where did he go?" asked Molly, looking around. They stood in a tubular, curving tunnel.

"He has to be in this tunnel somewhere; it's the only way. Come on, we'll catch up with him." The tunnel spiraled like a snail shell, getting bigger and wider as it wound around and around. Along one side grew thousands of tiny hairs that trembled and waved as they passed. "It looks like the amber waves

75

of grain. Watch this!" Max flung his hands out toward the hairs. They all lay down, then popped up again. Baxter scampered through the hairs, wreaking havoc.

"Look, another dead end," said Molly, as the tunnel ended abruptly.

"No, I see a trapdoor. Freewilly must be in there." Max pushed at the door and peeked through. "Freewilly, are you in here?" The door swung open and they crawled through into a great bony cave. A curious low sound peppered their ears.

Molly shuddered. "Where is that noise coming from? It sounds like rain."

"I can't tell. Maybe over there." Max pointed to the far end of the cavern, toward a huge round window. Stretched across it was a tight, vibrating membrane. Over their heads, three massive, oddly shaped bones linked together to bridge the cave. The farthest one was rooted to the center of the membrane. The near end of the bone bridge was the trapdoor. As the membrane vibrated from the sound, it rattled the bones until the last one tapped a message at the door.

"Hey, neat! A mobile!" said Molly.

"We're in the ear," said Max, "and those bones are the hammer, anvil, and stirrup!" He pointed at the membrane. "That's the eardrum."

"Baxter!" Molly grabbed him just in time. He had poked his nose down a hole and begun to crawl in. "Look, Max!" she gasped. "It's the back of the tongue and the epiglottis! For a second I thought this was a way out, but it's just back where we started—we'd get swallowed all over again."

Max came and had a look. "It must be the eustachian tube. It's an air passage to keep the pressure the same on both sides of the eardrum. Remember, the doctor told you yours was plugged up when you had that earache?"

A sudden light glowed in from beyond the eardrum, followed by a deafening BOOM. Sound waves hit the eardrum, bulged it in, and set the bone bridge to clattering. Max and Molly covered their ears. Baxter leaped in the air, then crouched in dismay.

"Thunder!" cried Molly, long before she uncovered her ears.

"Let's get out of here!" cried Max. They snatched up Baxter and fled.

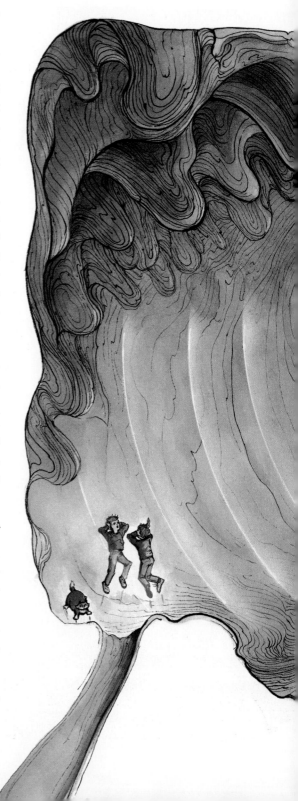

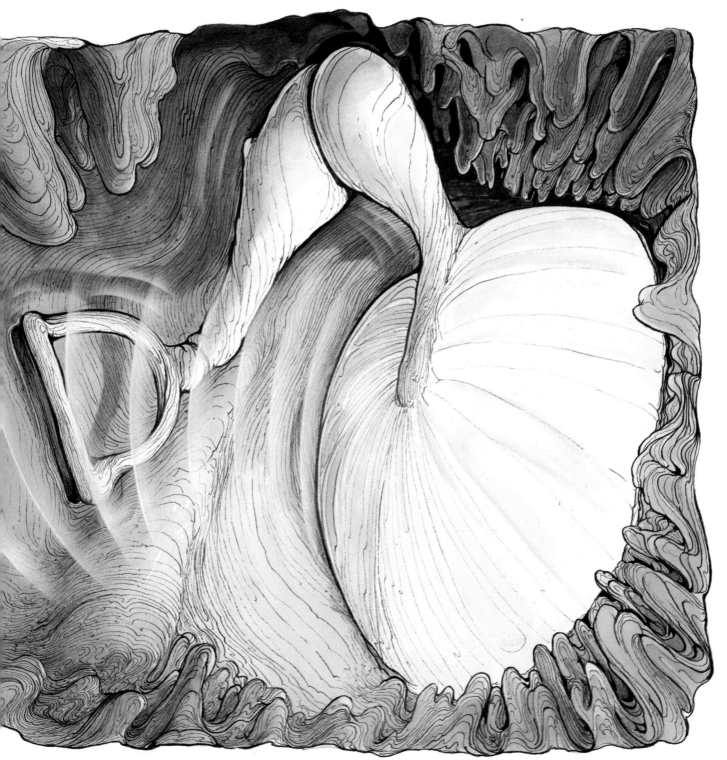

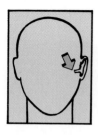

The trapdoor, now barely vibrating from gentler sounds, opened easily and let them through.

"What took you so long?" Freewilly sat in the entrance of a small tunnel leading off in another direction.

"Freewilly, where were you?" Max demanded.

"Right here. You were so busy scaring those poor little auditory receptors that you missed me." He pointed to the tufts of hair Max and Baxter had played with. "I can just imagine the garble they sent off to the Hearing Department."

"Those are hearing cells?" asked Molly. "We didn't know."

"Tell them that. They pick up the vibrations tapped on the door and relay them to the brain. They're the rods and cones of the ears."

Max went over to the tiny hairs, being careful not to step on any. Molly noticed Baxter had a gleam in his eye and picked him up. "Gee, I'm sorry," Max apologized. "I wasn't thinking." The hairs bowed and waved graciously in reply.

"How did you like the sound-effects department?" asked Freewilly.

"Interesting," Molly replied. "I don't think my head will ever be the same. You missed a good show."

"I can imagine!" he giggled. "But I never go in there, it's bone-dry. Besides, the noise might completely scatter me apart, and that would be curtains for Freewilly."

"I thought you were immortal," said Molly.

"Not if I got completely disassembled! Who'd put me back together? I'd also evaporate to death in there. So I stay out of the middle ear. This is the inner ear, nice and wet, so I like it just fine. Come on, I want to show you something really incredible." He popped into the tunnel behind him and disappeared. Molly went to the opening and started to crawl in.

"Wait a minute," said Max. "I'll bet this is another of his diversions."

"There's only one way to find out. Come on—I'm curious."

"Well, so am I, but I don't think it's smart to just follow him around like that. We'll be here forever."

"Just once more," said Molly. "If this doesn't lead anywhere, we'll have to make our own decisions."

"Last chance," said Max. They crawled into the tunnel and

found Freewilly sitting in a liquid-filled globe at the hub of three tubular arches that swooped up and away in three different planes. Molly looked up the tubes.

"Wow, they look like a roller coaster."

"Those," said Freewilly, making grand circles with his hands, "are the semicircular canals, the sense organs for motion and equilibrium."

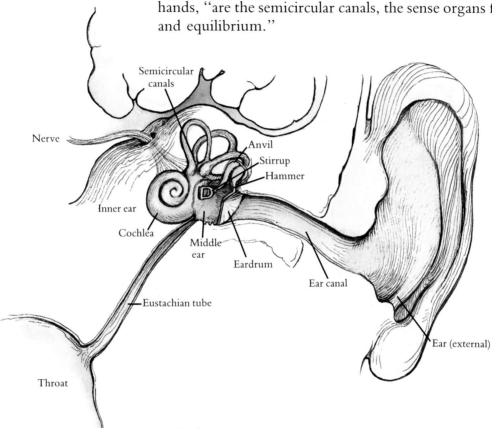

"I knew they reminded me of a roller coaster—now I know why."

"My liquid fills them. It sloshes when the head moves. Sensory neurons in the semicircular canals tell the brain how far, how fast, and in what direction it's moving."

"Why are there three? And at all different angles?" asked Max, peering up through the tubes.

"It takes three to cover all the possible directions. They slosh differently for each direction, and when they all slosh too much they get mixed up and make the Body dizzy."

"I think mine got mixed up when we were in the stomach," said Max. "I got seasick."

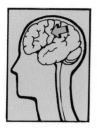

"Too much slosh." Freewilly nodded solemnly, giving a second opinion. Then he rubbed his hands together and looked around. "Let me see . . . where shall we go now?"

"Freewilly, you have to get this through your head," said Max. "We want to go home! Now are you going to help us or not?"

"Don't you like the inner ear?" Freewilly threw up his hands in dismay. "I thought you were enjoying it. It's *so* wonderful."

"It is," said Molly. "It's beautiful too, and very interesting, but also a dead end. We have to find a way out, Freewilly, we have to try!"

"Can't be done." Freewilly shrugged.

"Come on, Molly. Here's a nerve. It has to go to the brain— at least we know that much." Max marched away on the nerve. Baxter trotted after and Molly followed, Freewilly admonishing her all the way. They soon emerged from the hole in the skull and looked up at the great brain. Freewilly scurried ahead and waved them toward another hole with feverish gestures.

"Let's go this way," said Max, and he kept his course along the nerve. Freewilly threw up his hands in frustration and shook himself, sprinkling so hard he made Molly smile, he looked like Baxter shaking himself on the porch.

"Where do you think you're going?" he demanded, scooting back and flapping his arms.

"We're going back to the brain," Max replied. "The neurons are smart. Maybe they'll help us—you won't."

"They don't know as much as I do!"

"Maybe not, but they might be more reasonable." And he marched on.

Almost immediately on entering the brain they were lost in the tangle. Networks of neurons, trailing axons, and waving dendrites glittered and sparked and were full of useless information. Nobody knew about getting out.

"I am in Language," said one neuron. "I understand the word 'out' but I don't understand the concept. Perhaps if you try Perception they can help you. Just follow that corridor of axons over there, 325 doors to the left."

Perception sent them to Imagination, and Imagination sent them on.

"I'm in Guessing," said the next neuron. "Now let me see. Perhaps you could . . . no, that wouldn't do. Maybe . . . no, that would be just as bad. Actually, the only guys who know about doing things are in the Motor Acting Department. Yes, try them. They know about 'get up' and 'go.'" He gave them directions. Freewilly trailed along, contradicting them all and ridiculing their advice. Max marched on, determined not to give up. Molly followed patiently, gradually getting discouraged. Baxter began to complain. Their feet hurt.

"I am a motor neuron, and this is my girl," a bright neuron introduced himself and the neuron nearby. She nodded and twinkled demurely. "We met at work," he beamed. "We lift a finger, the right index finger, and we play the piano together." He smiled in her direction.

"It's the most important finger of all!" She added, "It's nice we're so close. Our finger must have the finest coordination. The Body's right-handed, you know."

"We share our work and our art. We give the Body its creative outlet, its fulfillment, its reason to live." They threw each other melting glances. "Without us, the Body might just lie down and die."

"Hardly!" said Freewilly, scarcely able to contain himself. He very nearly fizzed over. "Motor neurons are messengers, common labor. The brain does all that creating, not you. I am very closely associated with the brain— intimate, you might say— and I know! Artists, my eye!"

"Well," the girlfriend fixed him with a cool gaze, "we *are* the brain, in case you didn't know. And *we* play the piano, not you."

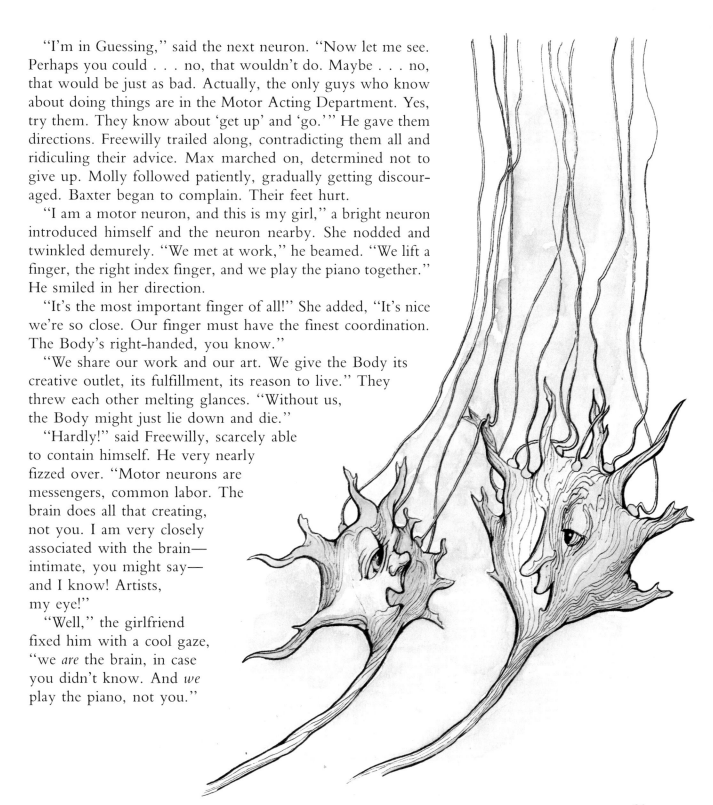

"Have you ever heard a piano?" Freewilly sprinkled spitefully. "You wouldn't know one if you did! Hearing neurons are trillions of synapses from here! And they wouldn't bother telling the likes of you, even if they could!"

"Come on, don't fight," said Max. "This is silly."

The first neuron glared at Freewilly. "You're just jealous because you're an insignificant little DRIP while we have brilliant artistic careers!"

Freewilly nearly fell apart. "Brilliant? You? If it weren't for me, you would just . . . DRY UP!"

Molly tried to make peace. "I think all jobs are important. If there's one thing I've learned here in the Body, it's that all of you need one another. And it's terrific to play the piano."

The neurons glowed with pride, but Freewilly flew into a rage. "If they could hear themselves play it, they wouldn't look so smug!" he screamed.

"But, Freewilly," said Max, "you just said they didn't play it at all."

"I DID NOT! Whose side are you on?"

"Nobody's side, we're just trying to get some information."

"Well, help yourselves! Those two motor morons are just what you need!" He cast them all a scathing glare and flounced away.

"Freewilly, don't be mad," Molly called and ran after him, but he had vanished in festoons of axons on their way to somewhere else.

"Where did he go?" she asked.

"Probably off to Emotions," declared the girlfriend.

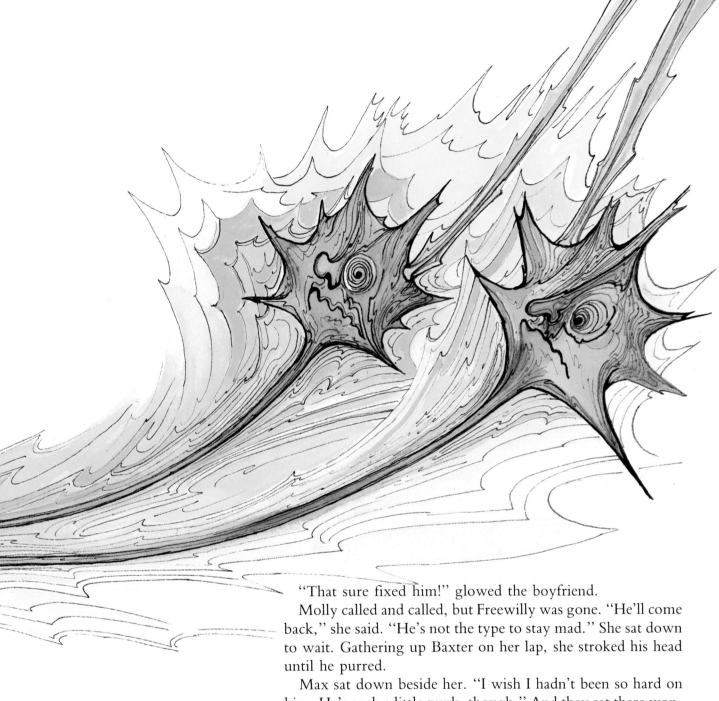

"That sure fixed him!" glowed the boyfriend.

Molly called and called, but Freewilly was gone. "He'll come back," she said. "He's not the type to stay mad." She sat down to wait. Gathering up Baxter on her lap, she stroked his head until he purred.

Max sat down beside her. "I wish I hadn't been so hard on him. He's such a little punk, though." And they sat there wondering what to do.

"Oh, yoo-hoo!" called the boyfriend. "I wouldn't sit there if I were you . . . ." But before he could finish, a spark slid in on a wire and depolarized him. He flashed with all his might—and the twins were sitting on his tail.

CHAPTER TEN

Instant lightning scooted them down the axon so fast everything blurred. They bounced through a synapse, got snatched up, and shot down another axon where they were dumped on hard red ground. Before they could move, the ground swelled, lifted itself up, and rolled over. The twins clung to the axon as the world turned upside down. Baxter dug in and stuck fast and watched them in bug-eyed dismay. They rode the upheaval to a terrifying zenith; then it paused, sank back, unrolled, and grew still, dropping the twins back at the foot of the axon. They cautiously picked themselves up and looked around. They were standing on a great tapering bundle of parallel, banded red cells. Long flat glistening white cables ran alongside, and they all disappeared together over a hill.

"Hello there." Molly caught her breath and waved to the cylindrical cells lined in tight rows under her feet. The long, striped cells lay perfectly still and eyed them in mute consternation. "Maybe they're in jail, they're all bound together and wearing stripes," she said. She picked up Baxter and waved his paw at them. "Are you allowed to talk?"

No reply. Max, who had been studying them closely, announced, "I think they're muscle cells," and that broke the ice.

Suddenly they were all talking at once. "Yes, yes, we are, we are. Muscle cells, in the muscle. Sorry we didn't answer sooner, we just couldn't believe you really came to see us. Nobody comes to see us. Ever. Well, the red blood cells do, but all they do is complain that we eat too much. Oh, it's so nice to have some real company!" The chorus rose.

"Wait!" cried Max. "We can't understand you all at once. Please, one at a time."

They chattered excitedly together for some time and elected one to speak for them. The rest contented

themselves with listening and nodding in eager, enthusiastic attention. After a significant pause, the elected spokesman cell cleared his voice and began. "We are voluntary muscle cells," he declared with all the dignity befitting his office. "You can tell by our red and white service stripes that we are the hard-working cells controlled by Conscious Activity through the Department of Motor Acting." He paused to let this sink in.

"We know," said Molly. "We just got a rather thrilling ride from there on an axon."

"OOOOOOO! How exciting!" All the cells wiggled and quivered in amazement, so much that Max and Molly nearly fell down.

"Silence! Calm down!" commanded their spokesman. "You're shaking our visitors up." The cells rustled and settled and finally were quiet, except for occasional trills, jerks, and flutters. "As I was saying," the spokesman went on, "it is a great honor and an occasion of great moment for us to receive visitors here in the forearm. Stuck as we are out here in the far limbs of the Body, hauling bones, we have come to be ignored by those inside. The important decisions and grand functions are all located far away from here, leaving us without representation adequate to our numbers, without"—

"Hey, skip the rhetoric and tell them about us," called a voice from behind him. "That's what they came to hear!"

"Yeah, tell them about us. After all, we have the most important job: moving the Body. Yeah, yeah," murmured the ranks. "Tell them that."

"I was just getting to that," huffed the spokesman. "I was filling them in on background material." Max and Molly got down on their hands and knees to hear him better and gave him their rapt attention. After a few more grand beginnings, the cell got down to business. "We are pullers, you see—muscles pull. My cell body, if you will be so good as to look closely, is packed full of parallel filaments. Some are like ropes, while the ones beside them are lined with tiny fists. When I get the signal to pull, my fists grab my ropes and yank. Then they let go, grab farther up and yank again, all the way to their ends, and all in a twinkling, too."

"Like a tug-of-war," said Max. "That's pulling in a rope hand over hand."

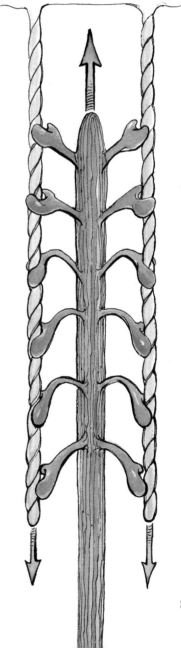

"Hmmm, nice description, I must remember that."

"Go on, go on," chorused the ranks.

"Where was I?"

"You were yanking your filaments," said Molly.

"Oh, yes. My fists pull in the ropes. Since the ropes are attached to my ends, that makes me considerably shorter."

"And fatter!" called the heckler behind.

The spokesman paused in stern disapproval and had to be urged to go on.

"Well, when the cells get shorter, the entire muscle gets shorter . . . and fatter. On one end, we're anchored to the arm bone. Our other end pulls a tendon, which pulls our finger bone and raises it up. We can move mountains when we work together!" he ended grandly, amid the polite applause of tiny filament fists. The elected spokesman grunted with pleasure and beamed through his red and white stripes. "It has even been said," he continued after a well-timed pause, "that we play the piano!" Cheers rose.

"You do!" exclaimed Molly. "We heard all about that in Motor Acting. We met your neurons."

"Oh! Please, extend to them my sincerest regards," said the cell.

"We'd be glad to," said Max, "but I doubt if we'll see them again."

"Just as I expected—I'm doomed. Out here in the sticks, so far from the real world, never to hobnob with the higher types . . ."

"If it makes you feel any better," Molly said, "we've been traveling around quite a bit in there, and nobody seems to be any better off than you. If you'd just think about how wonderful it is to lift a finger, and even to play music, you'd feel a whole lot better."

"But I'm destined never to hear it!"

"Don't pay any attention to him," said the cell beside him. "He thinks his talents are wasted on us. But I want to know, who would listen to him all day long if they weren't wrapped up and packed solid like we are?"

"You do look awfully confined," said Max.

"We are, but it goes with the job. It keeps us all yanking in

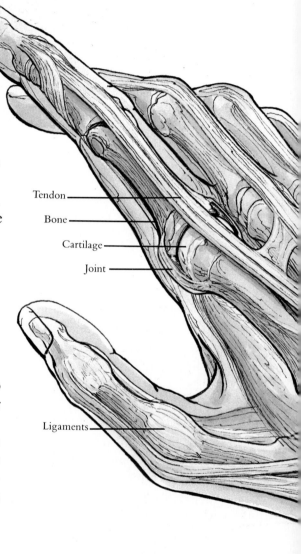

Tendon

Bone

Cartilage

Joint

Ligaments

the same direction. We just concentrate on the tendon. It reaches clear across the wrist and hand and plants into our finger bone. If you look around, you'll see lots of tendons on their way to fingers. See those flat white cables?"

Molly nodded. "But why do you live so far away? Wouldn't it be better if you lived closer to your work?"

"If we all crowded in down there, we'd make the hand so big and clumsy it wouldn't be able to move at all," the spokesman cell replied.

Max was flexing his fingers, watching the muscles in his forearm and feeling the tendons cross the back of his hand. "I guess it would be a problem if you all lived down there—hands would be muscle-bound."

"If you only pull and lift a finger, how does it get pushed back?" Molly flapped her finger up and down for them to see. A few cells gasped. "Did I say something wrong?" she asked. They were whispering excitedly among themselves. Finally the spokesman responded.

"There for a moment we thought you called that thing a finger."

"That's what it is." She held her hand up close to them. "See, I have lots." The whispering increased throughout the muscle.

"How do you come to have them?" asked the cell.

"We should have told you who we are. We're humans—this is what a body looks like." Small shrieks of dismay continued for some time. "We're lost and we're trying to get out. Do you know any way out of here?"

"I can only tell you where you are now: the back of the right forearm, near the wrist," said the cell when he had recovered. He studied Molly carefully while she studied her arm. "But to answer your previous question about the moving finger: other muscles live on the other side of the arm, and they pull it down. We work together."

Muscle

87

"I guess you're puppeteers—you pull tendons and operate the hand from way up here," she said.

"Hmmm, puppeteers, another nice descriptive phrase. I must remember that one too. A good vocabulary is so important to a public speaker."

"That's a surprise," called the heckler. "You never needed much more than 'I' or 'me' before."

"Ruffians, all of you!" the cell huffed and mumbled, then addressed the twins. "It is a difficult, thankless ordeal to represent the masses. But how, may I ask, have you come to be lost?"

Max and Molly explained all that had happened to them. The muscle cells listened in total silence. When they were finished, one commented, "We know all about Freewilly. You're better off without him—he never did anything for anybody. He thinks his precious water is all that counts, when we cells really do all the work. Water only does what we tell it to. He's a smart aleck."

"I know," said Molly, "but I kind of like him. I think he's ornery because he doesn't feel important."

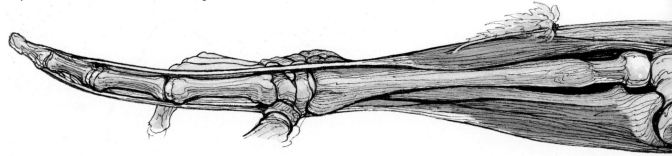

"You are too kind," said the cell. "We have to put up with him all the time, and he wears pretty thin."

"I still wish he were here," said Molly. She sat down on the nerve. "And I'm going to wait right here so he can find me, if he ever gets over being mad."

Max followed her. "I'm not sure he could if he wanted to. He won't know we got zapped down here, and those neurons would rather short out than tell him. Besides, he was really mad."

"We're sorry we can't help you," the muscle cells called.

"We wanted to have a chance to make our own decisions,"

said Molly. "So here we are. Any ideas?"

Max looked suspiciously at the nerve. "Are you sure that thing is safe to sit on?"

"Sure, it's the same one, axons coming in from Motor Acting. The worst it can do is bump us off and give us another somersault."

"That'd be enough"—but he sat down beside her just the same. Baxter hopped up on her lap to get petted and purr. "It's a long hike up that arm, maybe twenty miles," Max said glumly.

"Great. I was just beginning to feel hopeless."

"Come on, think lucky. Whenever we do, something comes along."

"Well, don't look now, something just did. We're moving." A quiet spark had risen out of the muscle and was whisking them up the arm.

"But how?" said Max. "I saw that nerve go right into that muscle."

"Maybe it's a two-way nerve. Maybe some sensory neuron is taking readings in the muscle," said Molly. "Muscles have feelings—mine sure get sore sometimes."

Max grinned and hooked his thumb over his shoulder. "Well, somebody is hitching us a free ride." They sped up the arm, around a bend, dived into a dark hole, and smacked into a tree. The tree rose over their heads farther than they could see and dropped down below them farther than they cared to look. They perched precariously on one of its highest branches.

89

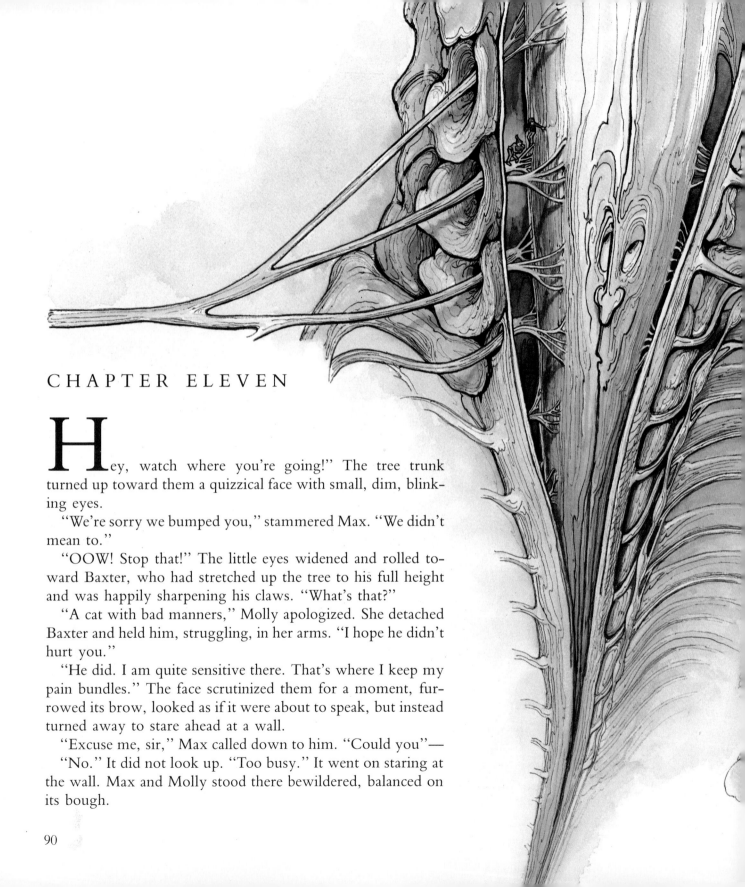

CHAPTER ELEVEN

Hey, watch where you're going!" The tree trunk turned up toward them a quizzical face with small, dim, blinking eyes.

"We're sorry we bumped you," stammered Max. "We didn't mean to."

"OOW! Stop that!" The little eyes widened and rolled toward Baxter, who had stretched up the tree to his full height and was happily sharpening his claws. "What's that?"

"A cat with bad manners," Molly apologized. She detached Baxter and held him, struggling, in her arms. "I hope he didn't hurt you."

"He did. I am quite sensitive there. That's where I keep my pain bundles." The face scrutinized them for a moment, furrowed its brow, looked as if it were about to speak, but instead turned away to stare ahead at a wall.

"Excuse me, sir," Max called down to him. "Could you"—

"No." It did not look up. "Too busy." It went on staring at the wall. Max and Molly stood there bewildered, balanced on its bough.

"He never says much. Don't feel bad," said a small voice behind them. They turned and saw a group of neurons that formed a large lump in the nerve. "Hi there," said one of them.

"A neuron!" said Molly.

"You bet. Sensory from the muscle. I just gave you a lift."

"Thanks," said Max. "We needed one. But what do you do in a muscle?"

"Me and my kind work in the muscles and tell the brain what's what around the Body. It has to know where its arms and legs are and how hard the muscles are working. Since our Human is always moving the Body, we have to monitor it all the time."

"Max and I are humans too. This is our cat." Molly kept a tight hold on Baxter as he wriggled and strained to get at the tree.

"You don't say," said the little neuron. "Who's monitoring you?"

"Nobody. We're lost. We were trying to ask that tree where we are, but it won't pay any attention."

"Don't waste your time, you can't distract him. He's not a tree, either, he's Spinal Cord: a solid tube of nervous tissue that goes all the way down the back. On the top, he sends his branches into the brain, and from there on down, he sends roots out all over the Body. You're standing on one now—we call them spinal nerves. Most messages between the brain and the Body get channeled through Spinal Cord."

"Wouldn't it be quicker for them to go direct?" asked Max, concerned that so sluggish and dim-witted a creature as Spinal Cord should have such a critical position.

"No, he's quite fast enough. Besides, lots of us neurons send similar messages. He sorts us out, bundles us up, and ships us up in tracts. You might say he keeps 'tract' of us." The neuron giggled at his own joke. "Get it?"

The twins laughed politely. "It sounds as if the Body has zip code," said Molly.

"Zip code, that's wonderful! Zip code . . . a perfect term for him, since he's so swift and efficient. But he is odd. I must tell you he has a most peculiar habit. He takes all of our messages, both going and coming, and crosses them to his other side! The brain is divided into left and right halves, so each half ends up with the opposite side of the Body. Isn't that wild?"

"But why?" asked Max.

"Nobody knows. He has never told anyone."

Spinal Cord did not tell them, either. He stared straight ahead at the wall with monumental concentration.

"He must be thinking about something terribly important," Molly remarked.

"Oh no, he doesn't think at all. He listens," said the neuron.

"He sure wouldn't listen to us!" said Max.

"Not to you, of course not. He was listening in on the incoming calls for signs of emergencies. He can pick up pain signals, switch on the proper motor neurons from here, and yank a muscle before the brain even feels the hurt."

"Like when we burn a finger," said Max. "My hand jumps back like lightning."

"That's Spinal Cord at work. Be grateful he was paying attention and not visiting with tourists," said the neuron.

"I see what you mean," said Molly. "Between the two of us there would be some very crispy fingers."

"Does he just sit and stare at that wall all day long?" asked Max.

"I don't think he has much choice. He's so precious, the Body built a bone tunnel around him just like it built the skull for the brain. His house is the backbone, a stack of cylindrical, squat bones sitting on each other all the way up the back from the hip bones to the skull. They're pillowed in between by cartilage disks and strapped together by ligaments that let them twist and bend. They have winged arches growing out of their sides, which make the tunnel for Spinal Cord and all sorts of interesting places for the muscles to grab hold of. Muscles need them too, because they have a tough and tricky job balancing the backbone on end with the whole Body hanging on it."

"It must be heavy!" said Max.

"You bet. But the Body is so ingenious! It made the bones lighter by making them hollow, then tucked all the red blood

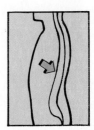

92

cell nurseries safe inside them. Then it polished off the ends of all the moving bones, coated them with cushiony, slick cartilage, and packed their joints in fluid. They're so light and slippery, the muscles have a much easier time. Believe me, I know, it's my job. The musculoskeletal system is a structural marvel, and the backbone is the architectural wonder of the Body."

"My skull sits on the top and I sit on the bottom." Molly laughed. "Come on, let's go out and have a better look." They thanked the little neuron and crawled over him out the hole under a bone arch.

"It's not a good idea to stand on the nerve," he said in parting. "Unless you want more rides."

"Let's crawl out on the bones," said Max.

"Up, down, or out?" asked Molly. "That looks like a rib going out here. It must be going around the lungs. Remember, the ribs make a sort of cage around them. Look, it's moving! It's breathing!"

"Let's not follow it, I don't want to go back to lungs."

"I don't want to go up, the brain is up there and it didn't help us too much."

"That leaves down. Let's go. This is going to be easier for Baxter than us." They began a long climb down along the wings and spurs of the backbone, occasionally sliding on ligaments. Nearby, ribs rose and sank gently with each breath. They finally came to a great thin wall. It bulged toward them as it crossed the whole Body, dividing the chest from the abdomen.

"Hey, that has to be the diaphragm," said Max. "It's the breathing muscle. It pulls tight and drops the floor under the lungs and pulls air into them. Then it lets go and it rises, and the air pushes out. They told us about it in gym—when we exercise, we're supposed to be sure and use it to get more air. It's called diaphragmatic breathing. I think the ribs help too."

"They must. Their lifting up makes the chest bigger, and that would suck in more air," Molly replied. "There's a slot in the diaphragm where this backbone goes through it, let's go that way."

"Okay, that will be the abdomen down there."

"You know, I've been thinking. According to that little neuron back there, all messages come down from the brain

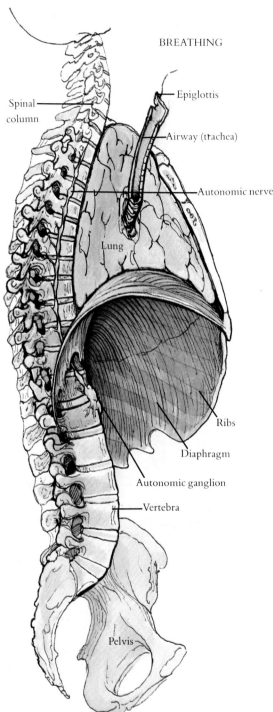

BREATHING

Spinal column

Epiglottis

Airway (trachea)

Autonomic nerve

Lung

Ribs

Diaphragm

Autonomic ganglion

Vertebra

Pelvis

93

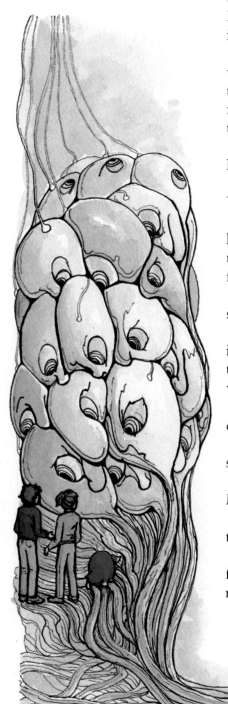

through Spinal Cord. We must have come down that way too. But when we rode back up, we couldn't get in—we smacked into it."

"Either the nerves going up toward the brain are smaller or we're bigger. . . . Oh, I get it," said Max. "But how can we tell, there's nothing to compare. We never saw any of this before. But come to think of it, that neuron was a lot smaller than the motor neurons were."

"And they were smaller than the visual sensory blue with the long number. It could be we're slowly getting bigger."

"I think you're right. I want to, anyway, but what changed? Where did it turn around?"

"I don't know," she said. "And there's something else. Why has the Body just left us alone? I'm sure it has surveillance cells that could catch us if they wanted. They must not be looking for us."

"I guess they don't think we're doing anything bad," said Max.

"That's just it. I've been so worried all along about *our* being in danger, but if you think about it, we're the real danger—to *them*. We're like germs. Most of the cells we've met have no way to protect themselves. They can't even move."

"They only have the Defense Department, and they're not chasing us."

"Let's be careful and keep it that way, and maybe we'll be safe till we find a way out."

"This is the best I've felt since this whole thing began," said Max. "We may have a chance."

They stumbled across a large lump of neurons as soon as they entered the abdomen.

"Who are you?" demanded a neuron. "And if you're looking for my shiftless partner, you'll find him over there in the adrenal gland, that way. Follow that nerve."

"Well, actually we were . . ." said Molly.

"Now don't bother me. I have this Body to run."

"All by yourself?"

"Me and my kind." The neuron rearranged its long arm. "This whole ganglion is a nest of neurons stuck with never-ending maintenance. We slave away, operating the organs, pumping, pounding, seeping, and squeezing, day in, day out, while nobody takes the slightest notice of us. Frankly, I'm sick of it—all responsibility, no fun. Unconscious Activity issues an order to the autonomic nervous system, and they pass it down to the parasympathetic nervous system, and they pass it down to us, poor old Basic Maintenance, the little people. We do all the work but never get any glory, no one's ever even heard of us. We're doomed to a life of toiling obscurity."

"We've heard all about you," said Max. "You run the heart, lungs, and stomach"—

"My, my, you *are* informed. What a surprise. My rascal partner usually gets all the attention, leaving me to drudge along behind the scenes. Then when there's a red alert, he jumps in and grabs the controls, screaming. As soon as it's over, he rolls over and goes back to sleep, leaving me to clean up the mess. Oh, well, at least I get some rest while he's in control."

"Emergency? Red alert?" asked Max. "I'm afraid I don't understand."

"Well, it's like this. I'm parasympathetic. We run the Body under normal operating conditions, but when the brain sends out an emergency red alert, signaling danger, the sympathetic emergency squads wake up and take over. They rev up the heart, crank up the lungs, pop out the eyes, and clamp down on intestinal arteries. That reroutes the blood into active duty over in voluntary muscles. Then they pump sweat out on the skin and adrenaline from the adrenal glands into the blood. And believe me, when adrenaline gets loose, everybody wakes up—it's the hop-up hormone! Those emergency squads are responsible for all the stress around here."

"They must be important," said Max. "Suppose the Body is in some awful danger—they would give it the energy to protect itself by fighting or running extra fast. Why else would the brain send out a red alert?"

"Oh, quite true," sighed the neuron, "but the brain makes some awfully dumb mistakes. Sometimes Imagination gets carried away and sends out red alerts, so the whole Body goes through pandemonium before we find out it's not real."

"I think that's what happens in a scary movie," said Molly. "I know it's not real, but my heart beats fast and I get shaky. I even get goose bumps."

"That's my partner fooling around at everyone else's expense. Goose bumps, nonsense!"

"Where is your partner now?" asked Max.

"Down that way, in the adrenal glands, and probably goofing off."

"Can we go see him? We're very interested in red alerts," said Max.

"Of course. Just follow that nerve fiber. Now I have to get back to work."

"Is it far?" asked Molly.

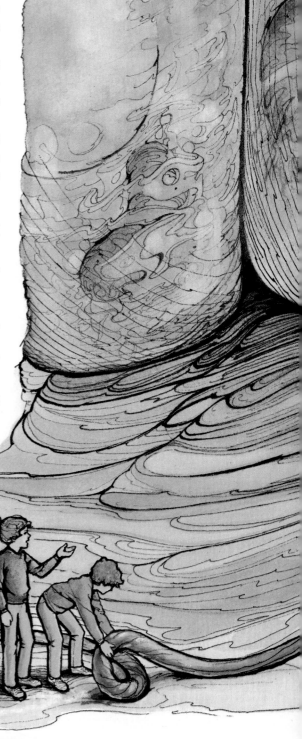

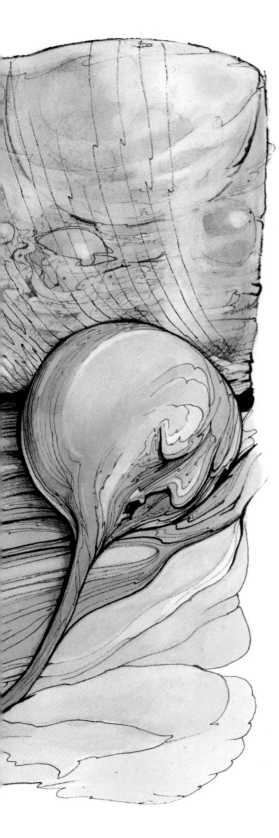

"No, the adrenal glands sit on top of the kidneys. You can see them from here." The kidneys were easy to make out, rising like dark red mountains on either side of the backbone.

"It looks like the kidneys are wearing hats," said Molly. "Do you mean those whitish things?"

"Right."

They hiked off. Baxter trotted along behind, pouncing on various unseen objects. "Why did you say we were interested in red alerts?" asked Molly when they were halfway there. Max had been pensive for some time.

"I got to thinking. Everywhere we've been, there's been some sort of catastrophe—lightning in the eye, thunder in the ear—even the motion of the arm could have meant some emergency. Maybe Spinal Cord reacted to pain or the Body was reacting to something outside. Something real."

"Or imagined," Molly added. "But if that's so, time would have to be practically standing still. Those reactions would be happening a split second apart."

"That's what I've been thinking about. Maybe we're so tiny that time is different for us. This heart beats a lot slower than mine. The reactions are happening in a logical order too. You see lightning before you hear thunder. And if you were afraid, you might raise up a hand, but that would take longer. It's just a theory."

"Oh, I get it—maybe this emergency neuron can tell us something about it. I never thought of that."

"Think lucky."

"Think lucky."

The adrenal gland turned out to be a small mountain of hormone-producing cells threaded through with capillaries and nerves. The twins trailed through it until they found the neuron. He was fast asleep. "That parasympathetic neuron sure was right," said Molly. "He's out cold. So much for his help."

Max shook the nerve fiber. "Maybe we can wake him up." But the neuron gave a few short snorts, mumbled incoherently, and sank into an even deeper sleep, snoring gently. Max looked around. "Maybe some of these other cells know what he's been up to—they're practically sitting on him."

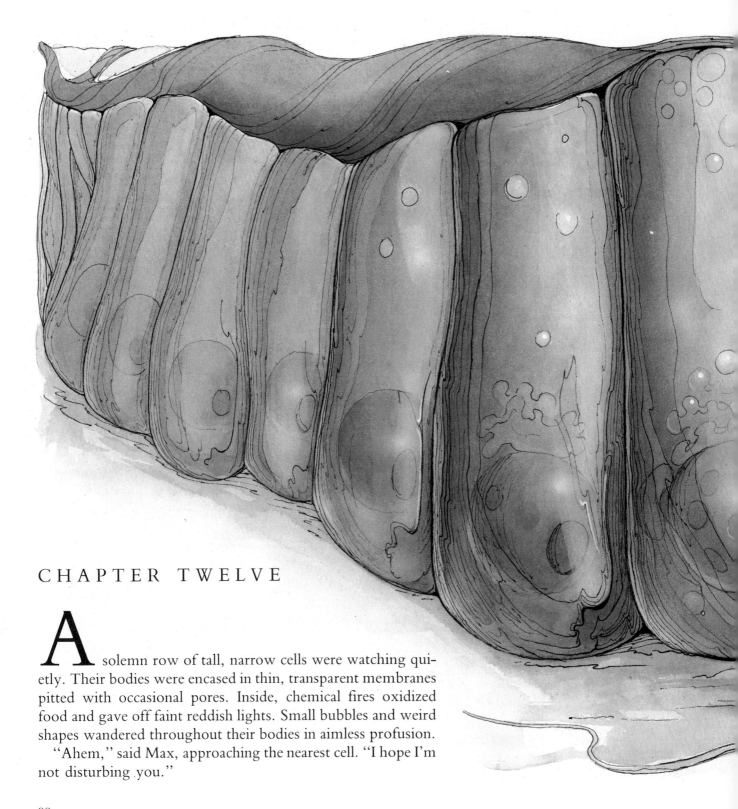

CHAPTER TWELVE

A solemn row of tall, narrow cells were watching quietly. Their bodies were encased in thin, transparent membranes pitted with occasional pores. Inside, chemical fires oxidized food and gave off faint reddish lights. Small bubbles and weird shapes wandered throughout their bodies in aimless profusion.

"Ahem," said Max, approaching the nearest cell. "I hope I'm not disturbing you."

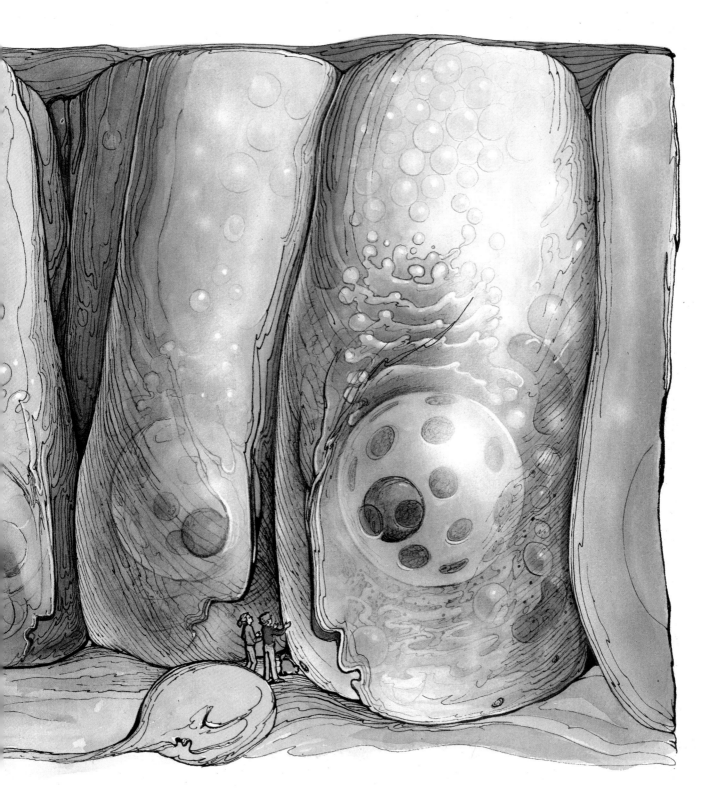

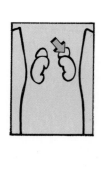

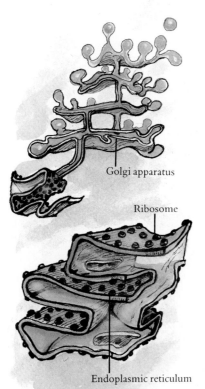

Golgi apparatus

Ribosome

Endoplasmic reticulum

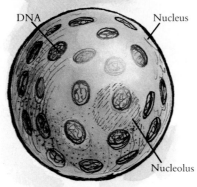

DNA

Nucleus

Nucleolus

"Not at all," the cell replied. "My body runs itself pretty well. Anyway, nothing much happens around here in peaceful-time, so all I have to do is manufacture my quota of hormone and pack it up. Look up at my top and you'll see I'm nearly full of bubbles. They're my product, adrenaline, waiting to be shipped into the capillary outside. I dump it in there all of a sudden, when there's a red alert." Globules filled his upper end. Beneath them many smaller bubbles popped out from the petal edges of a strange, flowerlike structure. They grew, pinched off, and floated up to join the others. "That's my Golgi apparatus," said the cell. "It gathers up my product and wraps it in shipping bubbles. It's my packaging department."

"Where does your product come from?" asked Molly, gazing into the jumble of shapes and objects chugging around inside his body.

"Look at my cytoplasm—my insides. See my reticulum; it's a maze of walls and canals. Ribosomes are those black dots living on the walls. They make the product and send it up."

The twins looked closely and saw a pattern of concentric partitions winding around his huge central ball. "Your reticulum looks like corrugated cardboard all rolled up," said Molly. Then she noticed the thousands of black dots attached to it, the ribosomes. "Cardboard with barnacles," she added.

"Ribosomes are my loyal workers," the cell went on. Just then a thin ribbon snaked out of a porthole in the central ball and slithered through the cell to a ribosome. It deftly threaded through it, hopped to the next, threaded through it, and went on to the next, stringing them like beads. "See that there?" said the cell. "Ribosomes getting orders from the DNA genetic code, which I store in my nucleus." He rolled the central ball to show them where that was. "My nucleus is chock-full of that code, on long computer tapes. They just print off the proper coded directions and mail them out."

"What a mess!" said Molly. "How do you ever find anything in there? It looks like my sock drawer."

"Oh, I tried to tidy it up once. I sorted it all and straightened up all the strands, but it just jumbled up again right away. I can't do a thing with it, so I've given up. Besides, they seem to know where to find whatever they're looking for, so I leave them alone."

"It sounds like my room," said Max.

"That's a lot of stuff in there," said Molly, looking closely at the mad melee of swarming ribbons inside the nucleus.

"It is. I've been given a complete set of the DNA code. That in there is enough information for me to go out and make my own Body—if I wanted to, and if I had the right facilities. I consider it quite an honor to be trusted with all our secrets."

"It is!" said Molly. "But what do you do with all those other things in your body if the ribosomes do all the work and the nucleus gives all the orders?"

"I have to eat, don't I?" said the cell. "They take care of me and give me the energy to convert the raw materials into product. It takes a lot to run this show, let me tell you that right now."

He wrinkled his skin. "My cell wall is my receiving department. It selects my food, oxygen, and raw materials from the blood. The food and oxygen go straight to a mitochondrion and get cooked up into chemical electricity. The mitochondria are my power plants."

"Could you show us one?" asked Max.

"I'll wiggle one for you." A long, pink, wormlike tube writhed slightly inside him. "See that? That's one. I have lots."

"What are the big round things, those over here?" asked Molly. She pointed toward some moonlike objects floating calmly about in the cytoplasm.

"My lysosomes. My disintegrators. Some receive raw materials and unpack and disassemble them for use. Others get rid of garbage, and some are the execution squad."

"What?"

"They kill any invaders that might harm me. They hunt down any of my parts that wear out, or quit, or just aren't working properly, and they eat them. They're full of strong, disintegrating digesters."

"Like in the stomach?" asked Max.

"I've never been there, but I've heard it's a tough spot."

"It sure is!" said Molly. "We almost got drowned in digesters. You're lucky you have them all safely bottled up."

"I'm sorry to say it isn't quite that simple. When I get too old to work well, or if I get badly hurt, my lysosomes will kill me too. They're always watching. That's why we call them executioners."

"That's awful!" said Molly. "I can't believe you have to live

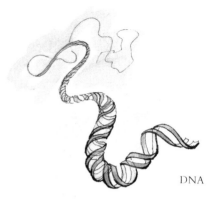

DNA

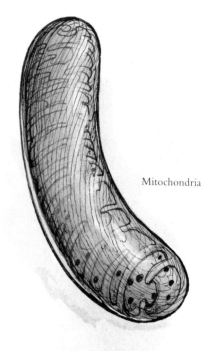

Mitochondria

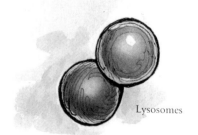

Lysosomes

like that . . . and feed them too!"

"It's the way of the Body. Any cell who doesn't do its job must die and make room for one who can. Only neurons live forever. The Body lets them get old and keeps them no matter how feeble and silly they get. But for the rest of us, this is utopia—we live only for the good of the Body. And the Body protects itself at all costs."

"I'm so sorry," said Molly, wondering how the faithful cell, devotedly bubbling up adrenaline, could discuss so calmly its own impending doom.

"SHRIEEEEEKKKK!"

They spun around, tripping over the neuron, who had leaped up in a shot of lightning. "RED ALERT!" he screamed in their faces, flapping and throwing himself into a mighty flash. "THIS IS A BIG ONE! EVERYBODY UP!!!"

"EJECT TOTAL LOAD NOW!!!" yelled the adrenal cell, as his adrenaline bubbles plowed up toward the capillary and exploded into it. Max and Molly and Baxter were caught in the middle between the neuron and the cell. His lightning flash hit them, wrapped them in glowing fingers, snatched them up, and flung them like bullets through soft, yielding walls into a tingling, throbbing sea of electric jelly. Then it withdrew and left them suspended, floating in firm space, dangling at odd angles. Max moved an arm. His body rolled over in a slow, weird revolution.

"Are we dead?" asked Molly. Then she saw Baxter floating nearby, upside down and wide-eyed. He meowed, trying to move, but he was pinned by invisible forces, imbedded in clear, thick aspic. "Oh, Baxter!" she cried and reached for him, only to spin away backward.

"Try scuba swimming," called Max. "Kick! This stuff is so thick, we're weightless."

Molly kicked tentatively and moved forward. She finally reached Baxter and pulled him to her. He clung to her and buried his nose in her neck, only peeking out during rare moments of courage. "Hang on, Bax, we're gonna get out of here," she said and kicked over to Max. He had righted himself and hung in the jelly like an astronaut space walking. He was looking up. Molly twisted to see a huge, pockmarked planet directly above. "Nucleus," said Max. "We're inside the cell . . .

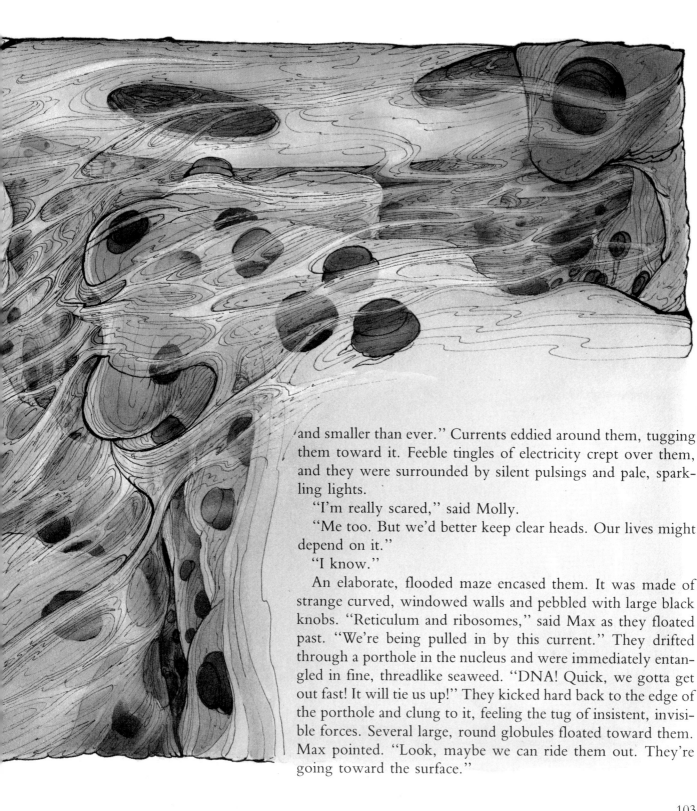

and smaller than ever." Currents eddied around them, tugging them toward it. Feeble tingles of electricity crept over them, and they were surrounded by silent pulsings and pale, sparkling lights.

"I'm really scared," said Molly.

"Me too. But we'd better keep clear heads. Our lives might depend on it."

"I know."

An elaborate, flooded maze encased them. It was made of strange curved, windowed walls and pebbled with large black knobs. "Reticulum and ribosomes," said Max as they floated past. "We're being pulled in by this current." They drifted through a porthole in the nucleus and were immediately entangled in fine, threadlike seaweed. "DNA! Quick, we gotta get out fast! It will tie us up!" They kicked hard back to the edge of the porthole and clung to it, feeling the tug of insistent, invisible forces. Several large, round globules floated toward them. Max pointed. "Look, maybe we can ride them out. They're going toward the surface."

"NO!" cried Molly. "Stay away! All the adrenaline bubbles got spewed out. That's an execution thing—a lysosome! Quick, hide in the hole. It's too big to come in here." They slid back into the nucleus and huddled under the edge of the hole, scarcely breathing, watching the lysosome cruise by. Loaded with a lethal dose of disintegrating digesters, patrolling for invaders, it scanned the surface of the nucleus, ready, looking for victims.

"That was close," whispered Max when it had passed. They pulled themselves out of the hole again. A mammoth pink dirigible churned overhead. Sparks of small static charges danced under its hull, and it glowed from the inner flame of its blast furnace.

"Mitochondrion," said Molly, "burning up food. I hope it doesn't think we're usable." Suddenly she felt herself grabbed by a violent undertow. It tore loose her grip and dragged her up toward the mitochondrion. "Help!" she yelled, thrashing and flailing and grabbing at space. Baxter peeked, moaned, and buried his head again, clinging to Molly with all four feet and wrapping his tail around her. Max leaped and caught one of her feet, but then he too was caught in the undertow. He spotted a ribosome attached to a nearby wall, kicked hard, and caught his toes under it. He yanked on Molly's foot with all his might and she came crashing down on him. Together they clung to the ribosome.

"Thanks," she panted, checking Baxter, still stuck to her like a large orange leech.

"Thank this ribosome," said Max, patting its squat round head. "Oh no!"

"Now what?"

"This ribosome. They were as big as basketballs only a few minutes ago, but now they're bigger than beachballs." More lightning probed the jelly, and sparks glittered along the undersurface of the mitochondrion. Before his eyes, Molly shrank. "We're shrinking away!" He stared up at the massive hulk with the gaze of a helpless submariner at the hull of a battleship. It dropped a depth charge. Light flared and they shrank some more. Electricity crackled. "That's it!" he yelled. "Electricity!"

"So what?" said Molly. "Anyone can see that!"

"No, I mean—that's what's doing this!" He yanked on her

sleeve and pointed up. "The power plant! Zapped! Lightning! We shrink when we get zapped, I just *saw* it happen."

Molly blinked. "But we didn't get zapped in the attic, or we'd be dead. Are we dead?"

"No, of course not. I don't think so." His face fell. "I thought I had it there for a second, but you're right. There has to be something else."

"Something else besides lightning or instead of?"

"Besides, I guess."

"What?"

"I don't know. Something in the attic, something different," he said. "What happened there? What were we doing?"

"Let's try to reconstruct it. You were looking in the book and showed me the tonsils."

"And you looked, and then BLAM."

"Yes, but I think there was something else."

"What? Quick, before we disappear."

"I was sitting there, and Baxter was walking on the page. I leaned over to look and held up the—Max! That's it! The magnifying glass! We were looking through it!"

"What?"

"Remember, I found it in the trunk. It made things bigger and smaller."

"Magnifying glasses can't do that."

"This one did. I tried to show you, but you wouldn't pay attention."

He groaned. "If that's it, we're done for. It's up there in the attic and we're here."

"No. It was in my hand." Molly plunged her hand into her pocket. "Empty. I must have lost it."

"Try another one. Here, give me Baxter." They peeled Baxter off and Max took him. He reattached, leechlike, immediately. Molly tried again and this time pulled out the antique silver-handled glass.

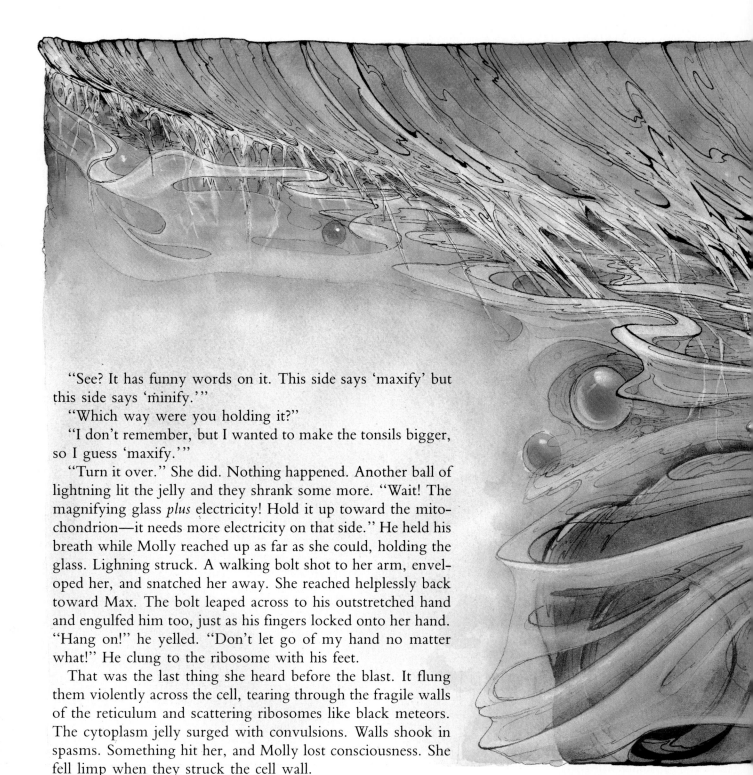

"See? It has funny words on it. This side says 'maxify' but this side says 'minify.'"

"Which way were you holding it?"

"I don't remember, but I wanted to make the tonsils bigger, so I guess 'maxify.'"

"Turn it over." She did. Nothing happened. Another ball of lightning lit the jelly and they shrank some more. "Wait! The magnifying glass *plus* electricity! Hold it up toward the mito-chondrion—it needs more electricity on that side." He held his breath while Molly reached up as far as she could, holding the glass. Lighning struck. A walking bolt shot to her arm, enveloped her, and snatched her away. She reached helplessly back toward Max. The bolt leaped across to his outstretched hand and engulfed him too, just as his fingers locked onto her hand. "Hang on!" he yelled. "Don't let go of my hand no matter what!" He clung to the ribosome with his feet.

That was the last thing she heard before the blast. It flung them violently across the cell, tearing through the fragile walls of the reticulum and scattering ribosomes like black meteors. The cytoplasm jelly surged with convulsions. Walls shook in spasms. Something hit her, and Molly lost consciousness. She fell limp when they struck the cell wall.

"Come on," cried Max, pulling at her. "We've got to get out of here. The cell is coming apart!" She didn't move. He grabbed her arm and dragged her along, holding Baxter too. Looking back briefly he saw the globules exploding and the nucleus tear, fold in, and shrivel. The dirigible mitochondria disintegrated and died in electrical chaos.

"Molly, wake up!" he screamed. He pulled her to the cell wall and tried to kick a hole through it. It was thick and firm, two fused layers of balls clinging together with amazing strength. It was heaving ominously. Max struggled along it, dragging Molly, until at last he found a pore opening. He crawled through and hauled Molly after him. Through the pore he could see exploding killer moons releasing something that was ravaging and destroying the cell until it collapsed and died. He pulled Molly safely away, felt her pulse to make sure she was alive, and sat down to watch and wait.

Finally Molly stirred. "Am I dead?" She opened her eyes.

"Almost. You got a bad knock." Max sat holding the magnifying glass. Baxter sat on her chest and purred ardently into her face, tickling her nose with his whiskers. She sneezed. "I think we're okay," he added. "At least we're bigger again."

"What happened? I remember trying to hang on and an explosion."

"We killed the cell."

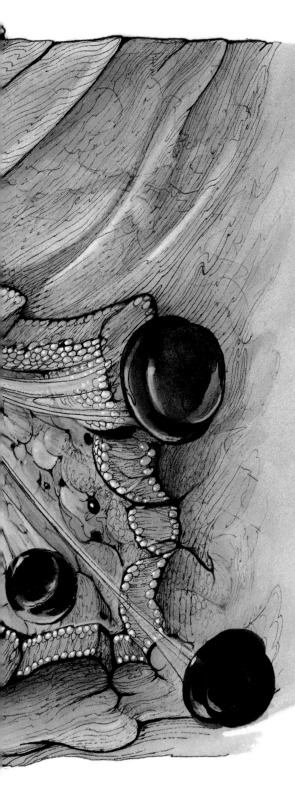

"What?" She sat up, wide awake. "Did we get out?"

"Yes, but not before we had damaged it so much it ate itself up."

"Where is it?"

"Was it. Over there." He pointed to a horrible gap in the neat row of cells. Molly got up and went over to look. The neuron was snoozing peacefully beside the hole.

"Do you suppose you other cells could move over just a little and fill this gap?" she inquired.

"No. We need a new cell to fill that position immediately, but don't fret, I'll take care of that right now," said one of the cells standing beside the hole.

"Wait a minute, it's my turn!" said the cell on the other side of the hole.

"No. You both got to since I did!" exclaimed the one behind.

"Well, only one gets to, there's only room for one, and we're only allowed to make one," said the first.

"I want to! After all, he made me," said the second.

"No, I made him, and I should be the one to replace him," said the cell behind.

"Me!"

"ME!"

"MEEE!!!"

"Wait," boomed the first. "Is this the way to show respect for our dead companion? May he rest in peace." They kept quiet, but not for long. They began to argue again.

Finally Molly intervened. "Why don't you go 'eenie, meenie, miney, mo,' like we do?"

"What's that?" they asked.

"I'll show you." She taught them the rhyme and how to count.

Eenie, meenie, miney, mo,
Catch a tiger by the toe,
If he hollers, let him go,
My mother told me to choose the very best one.

The cells rustled contentedly, and the two who lost were only mildly disappointed, they were so busy repeating the poem over and over to memorize it.

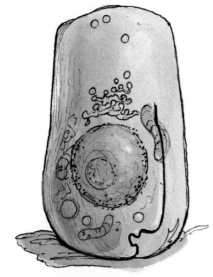

"Now," said the winner, "let me demonstrate the miracle of mitosis. First, I duplicate all my DNA computer tapes so I have two exact copies. Like this. Then, I'll coil them up neatly so they're easier to handle. I spiral them up and call them chromosomes." The tangled mess in his nucleus sorted itself into many neat crossed springs. "Then I'll just get rid of this nucleus." The wall around the chromosomes dissolved away. The chromosomes rushed out, pushing and jostling until they stood in a straight rank across the middle of the cell. "Now comes the fun part. ABOUT FACE!" The chromosomes pulled apart into two identical columns and marched to opposite ends of the cell. "Then I squeeze and pinch." The cell wiggled and sucked in his waistline until he popped in two. A new nucleus formed around each set of chromosomes, and they immediately unwound and jumbled up, making two hopeless messes inside two nuclei, inside two cells. "I'm hungry," said both. "Where is that capillary?"

"Twins!" said Max.

"Mitosis!" said one. "That's how we replace each other, by cell division. So you see, there's no permanent harm from your adventure, but I'd advise you to make yourselves scarce. The Body doesn't let anyone get away with murder. They'll send investigators, you can count on that."

"But it wasn't our fault!" Max protested. "We got bumped in by the neuron."

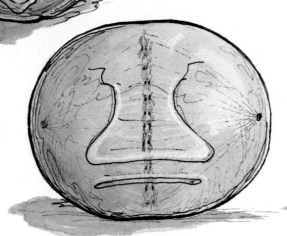

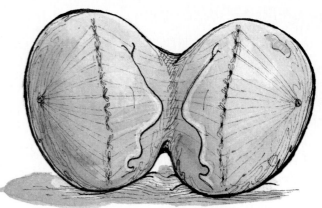

"He won't be much help to you—see for yourselves." The neuron snored quietly and rearranged himself more comfortably.

"If he's our defense," said Molly, "we'd better scram."

"But where?" asked Max.

"You could go hide in the kidney. It's right next door and it's very dark inside."

"We don't want to hide, we want to get out of the Body," said Molly.

"All the more reason to go there, it has contact with Out There."

"Hey, if you want to know all about kidneys, go across the border that way and see the adrenal cortex," said another cell.

"Good thinking," said the first. "We're in the adrenal medulla, but over in the cortex, they make a whole bunch of other hormones and run parts of the kidney by remote control. They're the waterworks department. Just go that way, only stay away from the nerves if you know what's good for you."

"Okay, thanks, and sorry about the trouble. We really didn't mean any harm," said Molly. "I feel just terrible about that cell."

"Oh, well, at least he went out gloriously!" the cell replied. "But before you go, was that meenie, weenie, eenie, ho? Or meany, mealy, mily . . ." Molly gave them one last hurried lesson. They left the cells behind, chanting the rhyme over and over and getting it all wrong.

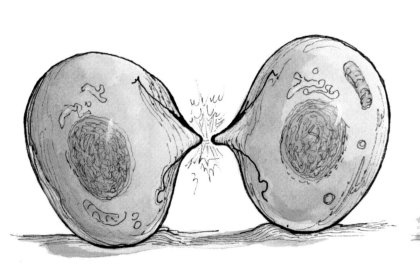
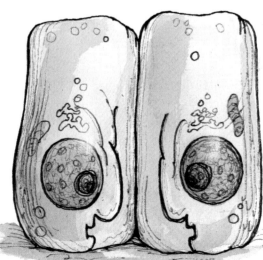

CHAPTER THIRTEEN

Y ou still have the magnifying glass," Molly said to Max. "Isn't that dangerous to carry around?"

"Yes, but we can't throw it away. How will we make ourselves big when we get out?"

"I just think we should be careful with it and keep it away from any more electricity until the time comes. We need some way to control it."

"You mean insulate it. How? It's all wet in here. The best we could possibly do would be to wrap it in something, maybe cloth, cotton . . . Our socks!" They quickly sat down and pulled off their socks and wrapped the glass in layer after layer. "Now how do we carry it? It's too big for a pocket." Max held up the resulting large wad.

"Under your shirt and tuck in your shirttail," said Molly. "I'll take care of Baxter and you take care of that."

"I just hope I don't make any more dumb mistakes."

"What mistakes? You figured it out!"

"I didn't realize the red alert would come after the lightning and thunder. But of course the brain had to process them before it could feel fear and signal emergency. I goofed, and almost got us killed. Now we're guilty of murder and they'll be looking for us all over."

"Oh. I wish Freewilly would come back. We aren't doing any better without him, and at least he knew where he was going."

Before very long, they came upon a group of short, squat, hormone-producing cells. "Slow down!" one was yelling at the others. "Drop production—imminent waterlog! Just got notice from pituitary, Body drank too much water. Pull out plugs, let excess go."

"Okay, okay, we can read too," another cell yelled back. "Sluice gates open. Bubbles down. Break time." They stretched and relaxed and began chatting among themselves. "Hi there," said one as the twins approached. "Want to join us?"

"What are you doing?" asked Molly. "Are you the water-works cells?"

"Only the managers. We control the switches—we make the hormones that regulate water release from the kidneys."

"We have an extremely delicate job," said another. Several nodded. "The Body must always be maintained at a perfect water level, even though it drinks at all different times. Then it sweats, and it breathes out moisture, too."

"It has even been known to cry," said another, "and that loses much more water than regular eyeball washing. All those variables make our job a real tough one. We must keep the Body from drying out, getting waterlogged, or even drowning from too much water in the lungs. We're the keepers of the overflow valves."

The cells had all settled down and attended with interest. "What can we do for you?" asked one.

"We were referred to you by cells in the medulla. They thought you could tell us about the kidney to see if we could get out of the Body there," said Max.

"Easy, no problem. Our kidney cells have direct contact with Out There, and they decide what goes."

"How can we get to them?"

"We talk to them through the blood, so follow that capillary back to the artery over there, keep going on the artery, and when you reach a really big one, take a left—you can't miss. . . ."

"Don't be in such a hurry," said another cell. "Stay and be sociable, we're on a break."

"I wish we could," said Molly, "but we have to go."

"Nonsense! This is the endocrine system—we take it slow and steady, except for the histrionics in the medulla. Come on, relax, it'll do you good."

"We really can't. You see, we had an accident

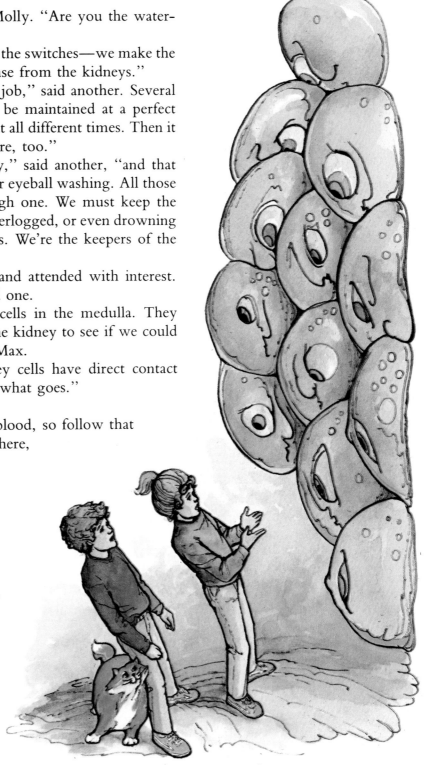

back there. This cell sort of . . . died."

"So what? Millions die every day from natural causes."

"This wasn't so natural," Molly went on. "We killed it."

Cells shuffled and murmured. "We're on the run," she confessed.

"Murder!" said more than one cell.

"It was an accident!" exclaimed Max.

"What difference does that make? The Body has *laws*. Murder is not permitted," said one cell, who took charge.

"But we didn't do anything. We were almost killed ourselves. We don't even belong here, we live Out There. It's all some big awful accident. We're innocent!"

The cells eyed them with distrust as Max went on to tell the whole story from beginning to end. "You see," he concluded, "it's all a mistake."

"The law's the law," said the cell.

"Please help us!" pleaded Molly. "We never meant any harm, and we only want to go home." She choked on a sob.

"Don't cry, little human. It leads to serious water loss and we'll have to go back to work." The cells conferred for several minutes, muttering, arguing, and throwing them occasional appraising glances. They nodded and shook, unraveled and consulted sections of their DNA codes, and finally reached a verdict.

The first cell spoke. "We have decided that, due to circumstances beyond your control, you are—guilty of murder." The other cells nodded in somber agreement. "But!" the cell continued, "not responsible. Therefore, we will not turn you in to the Defense Department, but we banish you from the Body."

"That's what we want!" said Max.

"That's all we ask!" said Molly. "But how?"

"I was coming to that. We're sending a message to the kidney to evacuate you. So you must go directly there and not get lost. Don't take any detours. They'll be waiting for you."

"Gee, thanks." Molly gathered up Baxter. "Don't worry, we'll hurry!"

"Remember, it's the first big left."

"Oh boy, we're almost out!" said Molly, breathlessly trotting along the artery behind Max. "Look, there's the big left." They entered a cave in the dark mountain of the kidney. The

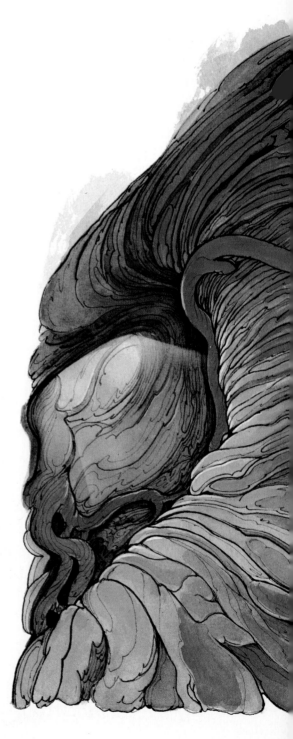

great artery soon branched into tiny arteries, which finally ended in large, knotted balls of twisted capillaries.

"This looks a lot like Grandma's tomato patch," said Max. Huge red bulbs, each filled with a capillary knot, hung on long, twining stems. Molly peeped in the opening of one of the bulbs.

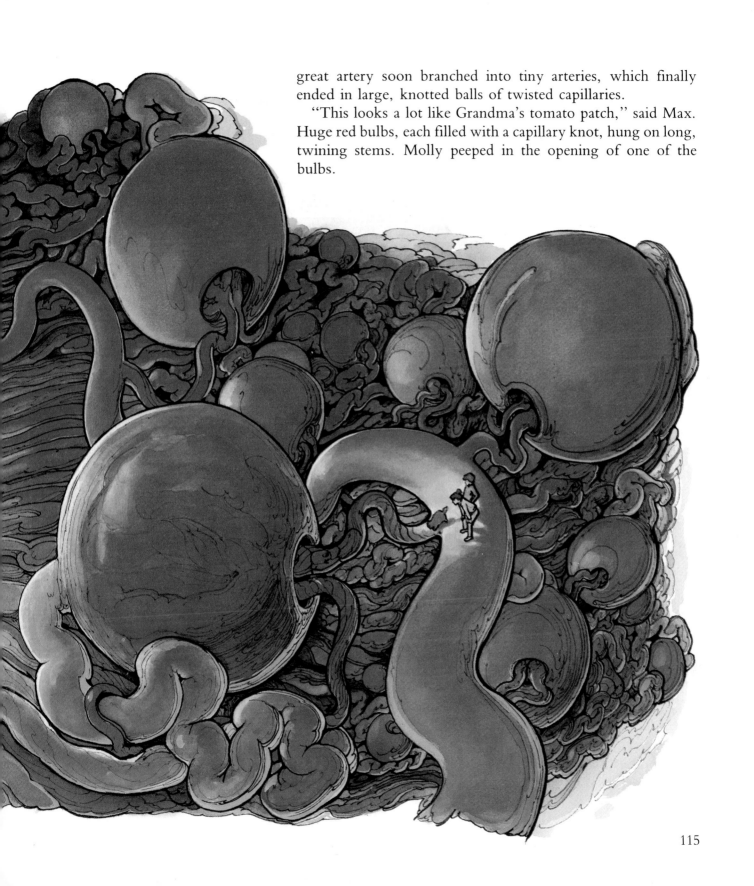

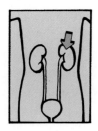

"I wouldn't go in there if I were you," warned a cell living at the edge of the opening. "We're squeezing blood in there." Molly jumped back. "Perfectly normal," said the cell. "It's our job in this part of the nephron; we wring out the blood. This is the laundry department. We take the dirty blood, all full of cell wastes, and filter it clean."

"Oh," said Max. "They told us in the adrenal gland that you regulate water levels."

"That's farther down." The cell rolled its nucleus in the direction of the long, twisting vines. "Those tubules are in charge of water flush and recovery. I just see to the squeezings. We wring the water and wastes out of the blood in here"—he indicated the capillary knot—"and send them off in the tubule. Then we send the blood on, still full of cells but considerably less wet. The tubule sorts out the fluid, decides what to keep, and returns just the right amount of water back to the blood. But that all goes on down there."

"That must be where we're supposed to go," said Max. "We're supposed to report for evacuation."

"That's the place. Follow my tubule until it gets skinny and makes a hairpin turn—that's the sluice gate where they decide what gets out."

The tubule resembled a snake tied in knots. They hiked along, stepping over capillaries, and came to the hairpin turn.

"You're late!" a cell in the tube wall yelled at them. "Where have you been?"

"Who are you?" asked Molly.

"Transport! Waterworks Department. We run the pumps."

"You pump water?"

"Certainly not! We pump salt!"

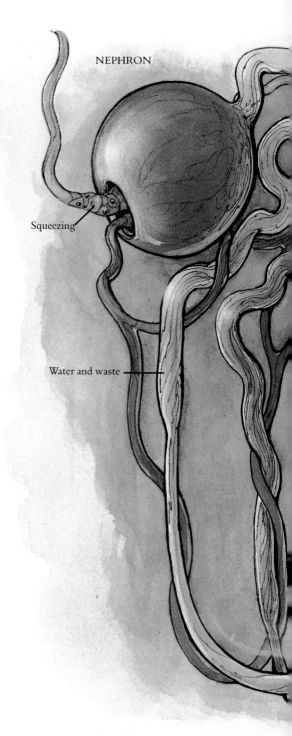

NEPHRON

Squeezing

Water and waste

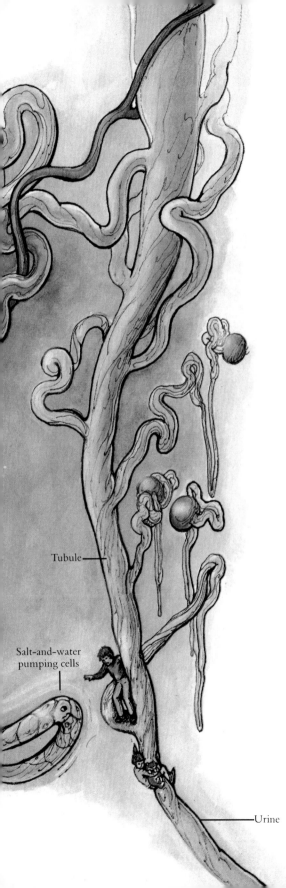

Tubule

Salt-and-water
pumping cells

Urine

"Salt!"

"Of course, and water follows. Believe me, if you ever want to do anything with water, use salt. Water can't resist following salt. That's my job, manipulating their attractions to each other. I get my orders from the adrenal cortex so I know how much salt to pump and when. The salt and then the water re-join the blood in that capillary you're standing on. The blood in there is semidry and hankering for water. But when we're all done, the blood is back to normal and we have all the wastes and excess water here in our tube to be disposed of."

"That would be urine in the tube," said Molly.

"Right," said the cell. "Now get cracking and squeeze in, I have orders to transport you out."

"Wait a minute," said Max, putting a restraining hand on Molly's arm. "Just what's in the urine?"

"Water, wastes, junk, just like I said."

"What about oxygen?"

"Certainly not! What do you take us for, idiots? Oxygen is a valuable commodity, we don't throw that away."

"Then we're not going! We'd drown!"

"Nonsense. My job is to keep the Body from drowning—haven't you been listening?"

Max patiently repeated their story and explained why they would never survive in urine.

The cell listened, then it said, "I see your point. You'd better not be standing on that capillary."

"Why not?"

"If white blood cells in there are after you, they can easily spot you through the wall and slide out between the cracks. They do it all the time."

"Yikes!" cried Molly, trying to pick up both feet at once.

"Here, I'll swing you away over to the big sewer line, the collecting tube, and you can get away along the ureter. All the tubules run together down there." The cell enlisted all the nearby cells in the loop, and the twins and Baxter climbed onto it and were swung far away from the capillaries to a tall, branched pillar. They crawled down from branch to branch, slid down its slippery trunk, and landed on the huge ureter, the great sewer pipe that stretched away along the inside of the Body wall.

117

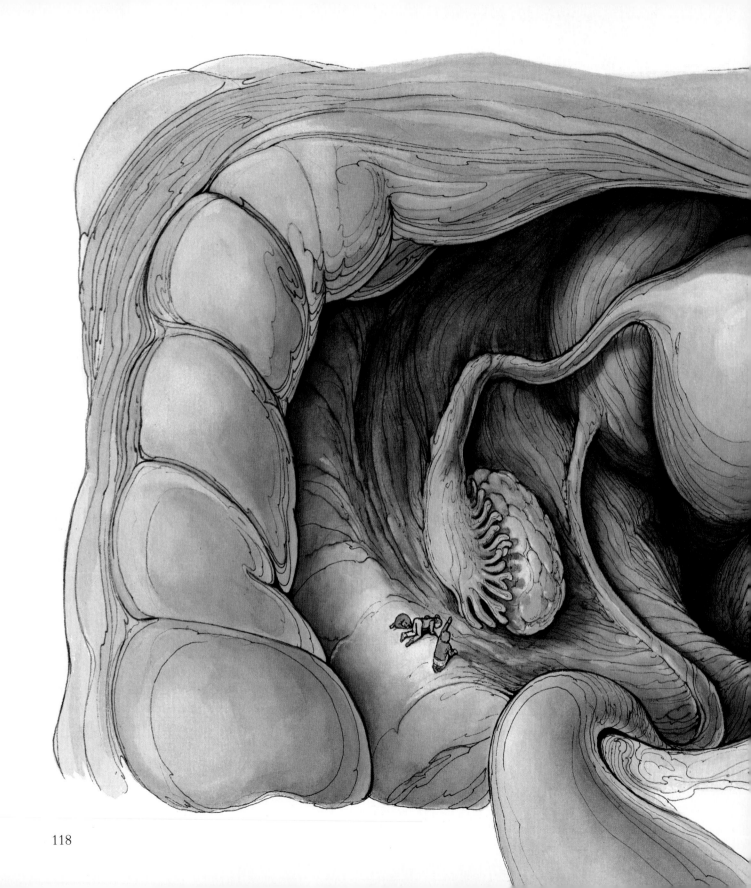

118

CHAPTER FOURTEEN

T hat was close!" said Molly. "We'd better watch our step!"

"Did that cell say we should escape along the ureter?"

"Yes. I guess he meant to follow it. Wow! Look up!" Great, soft, folding loops packed the abdomen above them. "That's got to be the small intestine seen from the outside."

Molly put Baxter down and he trotted off on the ureter. The twins trailed behind, looking up. "That's the large intestine," said Max, pointing at a gigantic, bulbous length of intestine. It hung overhead and draped across the lower end of the abdomen toward the center, where it turned and plunged into a deep, tapering pit. The ureter reached the edge of the pit and plummeted into it, then climbed up the other side, ending in a huge, muscular dome stuck to the opposite wall. "That's the bladder," said Max. "It stores the urine."

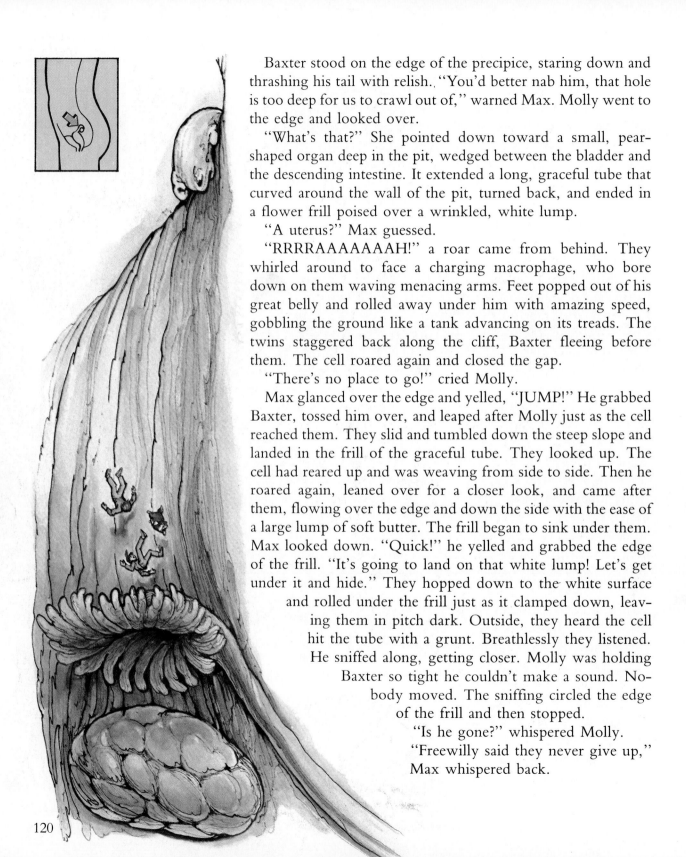

Baxter stood on the edge of the precipice, staring down and thrashing his tail with relish. "You'd better nab him, that hole is too deep for us to crawl out of," warned Max. Molly went to the edge and looked over.

"What's that?" She pointed down toward a small, pear-shaped organ deep in the pit, wedged between the bladder and the descending intestine. It extended a long, graceful tube that curved around the wall of the pit, turned back, and ended in a flower frill poised over a wrinkled, white lump.

"A uterus?" Max guessed.

"RRRRAAAAAAAH!" a roar came from behind. They whirled around to face a charging macrophage, who bore down on them waving menacing arms. Feet popped out of his great belly and rolled away under him with amazing speed, gobbling the ground like a tank advancing on its treads. The twins staggered back along the cliff, Baxter fleeing before them. The cell roared again and closed the gap.

"There's no place to go!" cried Molly.

Max glanced over the edge and yelled, "JUMP!" He grabbed Baxter, tossed him over, and leaped after Molly just as the cell reached them. They slid and tumbled down the steep slope and landed in the frill of the graceful tube. They looked up. The cell had reared up and was weaving from side to side. Then he roared again, leaned over for a closer look, and came after them, flowing over the edge and down the side with the ease of a large lump of soft butter. The frill began to sink under them. Max looked down. "Quick!" he yelled and grabbed the edge of the frill. "It's going to land on that white lump! Let's get under it and hide." They hopped down to the white surface and rolled under the frill just as it clamped down, leaving them in pitch dark. Outside, they heard the cell hit the tube with a grunt. Breathlessly they listened. He sniffed along, getting closer. Molly was holding Baxter so tight he couldn't make a sound. Nobody moved. The sniffing circled the edge of the frill and then stopped.

"Is he gone?" whispered Molly.

"Freewilly said they never give up," Max whispered back.

"But I don't hear—HEEELP!!!" she screamed. A thin, rubbery tentacle had slithered under their protecting hood and whipped around her ankle. Max groped in the dark and grabbed hot, wet, oozing rubber. His hand sank in and stuck fast. The frilly tube sprang up and light flooded in, silhouetting the roaring monster. He bellowed in triumph, drooled, and opened a cavernous mouth. Baxter hissed and struck. His paws stuck fast. The twins struggled and clawed at the ground, but the cell dragged them closer.

"Stop!" commanded a frantic voice. Suddenly a tiny creature flitted up to the monster's face. The monster brushed it away, scarcely noticing. It immediately returned with a more violent attack, kicking and pummeling with tiny fists, buzzing and shrieking with the fierceness of a demented mosquito.

"Freewilly!" cried Molly. The monster slapped again, sending Freewilly splattering against the wall, where he sagged, then slid slowly down, like a lone tear. He struggled to rise.

"NO!" yelled Max. "Freewilly, stay away, you'll get killed!" But Freewilly roused himself, gathered himself up in a tight ball, and hurled himself with all his strength. He plowed hard and straight into the monster's nose.

"OOOOOF!" it grunted and turned on him, swinging and slashing. Freewilly staggered but dodged away. The cell swung again, this time knocking off several sizable drops. Severely weakened and diminished, Freewilly fought on. The twins and Baxter were dragged along as the battle raged. They rolled and tumbled down deeper and deeper into the pit. Freewilly had shrunk to an exhausted, pitiful fleck, but he wouldn't give up. Finally, the cell slumped in a heap. "I have to rest."

"It's about time, you big fat slug!" squawked Freewilly, hanging on the wall and gasping.

"Shut up, you litle squirt. I'm going to wring you dry in just a minute. You haven't gotten away— nobody gets away

from a macrophage. Don't you know you're obstructing justice? I have orders to demolish this gang."

Freewilly scorched him with a glance. "Go ahead, you big fool, eat them. See what happens. You'll be sorry."

"Freewilly, no!" cried Molly. He ignored her.

"You're just like the rest of them. I see it all over the Body. One big meal and pffft!" He waved goodby, wet fingers dribbling.

"What are you talking about?" asked the cell.

"I just told you, stupid, eat them and die. Go on, see for yourself." He urged him on by flipping his wrists.

"They never told me that," said the cell.

"Did you ever see a macrophage *after* he ate a big one?" The cell shook his head. "Go on, eat them and find out." Freewilly floated away to gather up droplets, humming. The big cell pondered. He studied his struggling prey. Molly whined, "Please, don't . . ." He consulted his DNA tapes and spoke.

"I have to," he sighed. "It's my job, no matter what happens to me. I serve the Body, and those are my orders. I cannot disobey."

"But why?" cried Max. "What have we done?"

The cell swelled up fiercely. "Plenty!" he bellowed. "You harbor an alien, a cat-thing. You are parasites with no meaningful work. You are charged with infractions of disturbing the peace in the blood. But most of all you are *murderers!*"

"We were acquitted," said Max meekly.

"You were banished and you refused to go!"

"We would have died!" cried Molly.

"That's beside the point," said the cell. "It looks as if this is going to kill me too. But orders are orders. Wouldn't you know I'd be dumb enough to sign up for suicide. You never hear about the bad side around here, they just promise you the glory . . . Why, I thought I'd get a citation or something for catching you."

"What are your orders, exactly?" Max asked suddenly.

"To get rid of you and the cat-thing."

"That's all? Just to get rid of us?"

"That's enough." He burped. "What a day to have indigestion. I feel worse every minute."

"That's because you know we're not really bad," said Max.

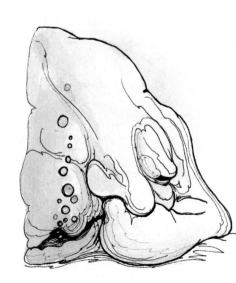

"Why waste your life on us? You could follow your orders and still save yourself for a real danger someday."

"How?"

"You could get rid of us by getting us out!"

The macrophage considered this. "Yes, but I don't have the slightest idea how to do that. We don't even discuss it around here." He belched again and looked even more miserable.

They all sighed in mutual dilemma and despair.

"I know a way out," said Freewilly. "Lymph." Max and Molly sat up and stared. "Lymph, my own private waterway. It goes everywhere and you'd be safe because nobody knows about it but me."

"You knew about it all along and you never told us?" demanded Molly. "How could you?"

Freewilly smiled weakly and shrugged. "I never thought it would come to this, really. I just figured you'd get used to it here and stay. I get awfully lonesome in here. You may have noticed I'm not too popular with cells."

"If you weren't such a selfish little stinker, you could"— Max exclaimed. He struggled against the cell's grasp to get at Freewilly.

"Max!" cried Molly. "He just tried to save us! Can't you see, he's finally done something generous!"

"I can hardly believe it myself," said Freewilly, "but I got to kind of like you."

Max stopped. "You did try. I guess I should thank you for that. But what made you come back after you were so mad?"

"I kept hearing stories about how things were going with you and I began to realize you really can't live here. Then I remembered how you were always so nice and polite to me even when I was a little stinker. Nobody was ever respectful to me before. Nobody ever even paid me any attention or showed me how to behave or have friends. They just think I'm a useless little drip they can order around."

"That's not true," said Molly. "You're essential to them all! And you were so helpful to us! You know all about the Body, and you taught us so much!"

"But that's not important. It's not like being a real cell with a real job!"

"Oh, Freewilly, you could have the best job of all! You could go around and teach all the cells about each other. They would be so grateful. They're stuck down and nobody ever tells them anything, so they have the most peculiar ideas! You could tell them how they all need each other and are helping each other . . ."

Freewilly giggled shyly. "Do you really think so?"

The macrophage nodded soberly. "You just taught me something, even if I'm not too thrilled about it. I'd rather be knowing than not knowing. At least I know what the deal is now."

Max was struggling in the cell's grip. "Are we going to get going or not?"

"If we can get you out through the lymph," said the cell, "I have no objections. I'd even prefer that. It would save my life too."

"Where is lymph?" asked Molly as the cell released them.

"All around you," said Freewilly. "It's blood without blood cells. It filters out of the capillaries to carry food to the cells. The excess gets drained off by lymph vessels, carried up to the neck, and dumped back into the blood. It's pure body fluid. It's all me!" Max and Molly smiled at each other. Freewilly was up to speed and rolling. "I think the best plan is to get you up to the neck. Just before the lymph goes back into the blood, it's very close to the skin. I can get you out from there."

"I'll give you a lift," said the cell. "I have to be sure you go." He made a deep pocket in his back, and they all crawled in.

"I hope he doesn't get hungry," whispered Molly as she felt his soft cytoplasm fold around them.

"At least we'll look half eaten if any other cells see us," Max murmured.

"This way!" called Freewilly, and the cell lumbered off toward a nearly invisible transparent vessel filled with clear fluid.

"I can see why we never noticed them before," said Molly as they squeezed through its loose wall and floated up out of the pit.

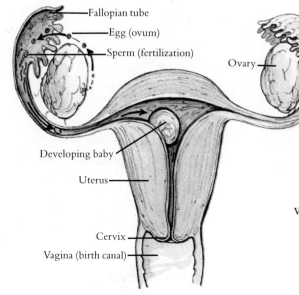

FEMALE REPRODUCTIVE TRACT

Fallopian tube
Egg (ovum)
Sperm (fertilization)
Ovary
Developing baby
Uterus
Cervix
Vagina (birth canal)

"I'm so glad you came back, Freewilly," said Molly. "And just in the nick of time."

The cell chuckled. "It's a good thing you thought of that trick with the fallopian tube, or it would have been too late."

"Is that what that flower frill was?" asked Molly.

"Sure was," said the cell, "and that white lump you were sitting on is an ovary."

"Isn't the ovary where the eggs are stored?"

"About a thousand eggs," said Freewilly. "One pops out of an ovary once a month and into the fallopian tube. It transports the egg into the uterus."

"We saw the uterus; it looked pear-shaped and sat behind the bladder. The tube came out of its side."

"There's another ovary and tube on the other side too. So much of the Body is symmetrical, you know. Anyhow, as I was saying, if an egg gets fertilized by a sperm as it goes down the tube, it plants itself in the uterus and grows into a baby there. The uterus can stretch big enough to hold a whole baby, then it squeezes and the baby gets born and voilà!"—he snapped wet fingers—"a brand-new little human!"

"A thousand babies," Molly mumbled.

"You know," said Max, "the Body has to be a male or a female, but it never occurred to me to wonder which."

"Lucky for you it's a female," said Freewilly.

"Why?"

"Because you wouldn't have had a fallopian tube to hide under in a male. Instead of ovaries, males develop testicles, which make millions and millions of sperm. Testicles travel out through the Body wall by way of a canal and take up residence Out There in a sack. The only traces they leave behind are the tubes that carry the sperm. Even the canal seals off, so you see, there would have been no place to hide. Male and female are pretty much the same otherwise. On the inside, at least."

MALE REPRODUCTIVE TRACT

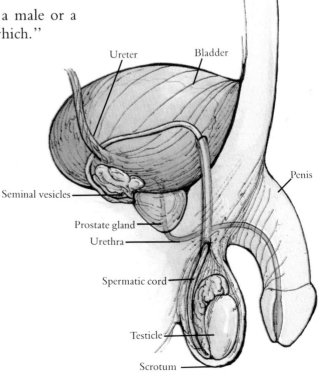

Ureter

Bladder

Seminal vesicles

Penis

Prostate gland

Urethra

Spermatic cord

Testicle

Scrotum

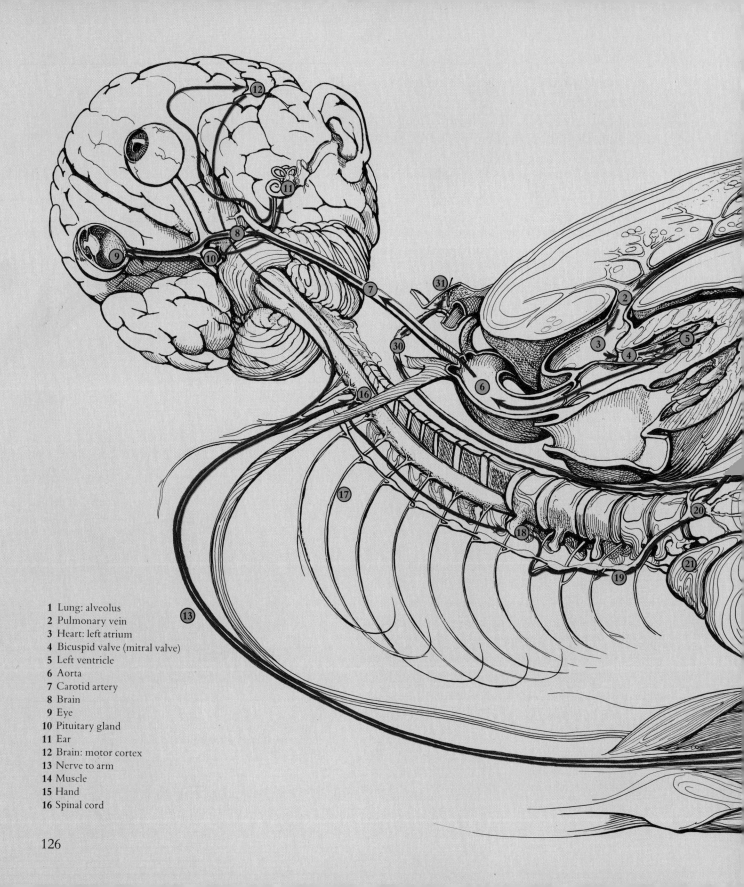

1 Lung: alveolus
2 Pulmonary vein
3 Heart: left atrium
4 Bicuspid valve (mitral valve)
5 Left ventricle
6 Aorta
7 Carotid artery
8 Brain
9 Eye
10 Pituitary gland
11 Ear
12 Brain: motor cortex
13 Nerve to arm
14 Muscle
15 Hand
16 Spinal cord

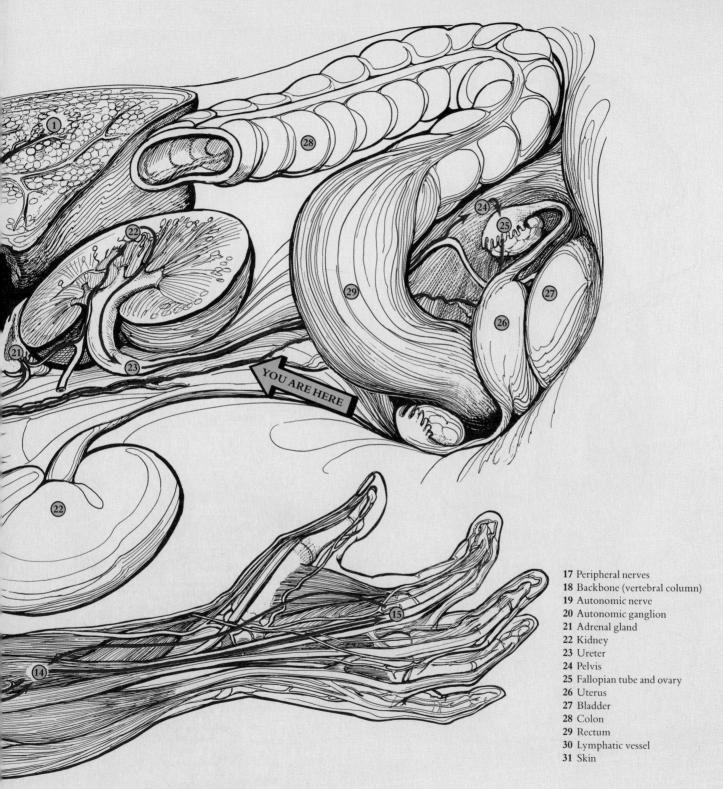

YOU ARE HERE

17 Peripheral nerves
18 Backbone (vertebral column)
19 Autonomic nerve
20 Autonomic ganglion
21 Adrenal gland
22 Kidney
23 Ureter
24 Pelvis
25 Fallopian tube and ovary
26 Uterus
27 Bladder
28 Colon
29 Rectum
30 Lymphatic vessel
31 Skin

127

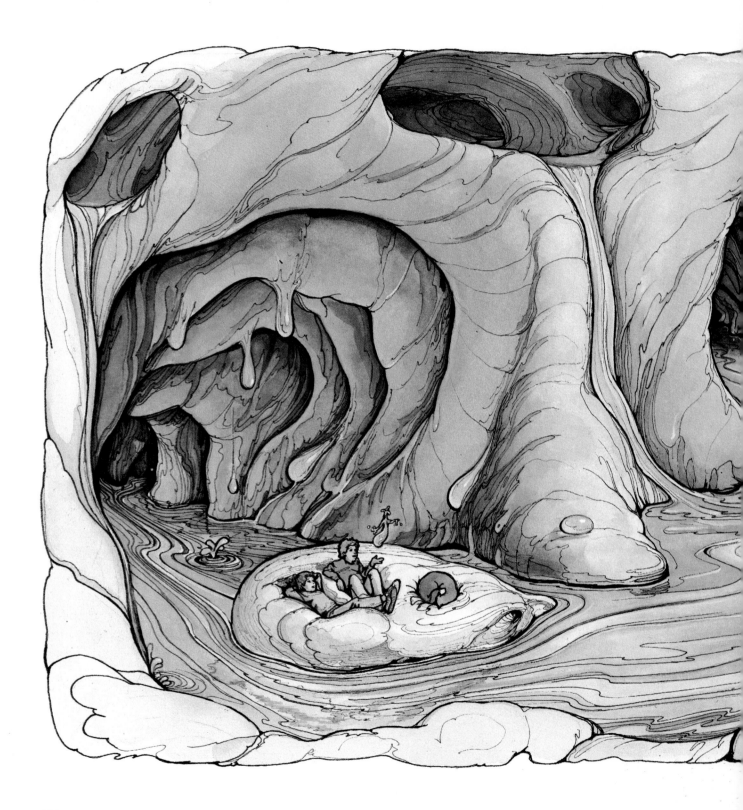

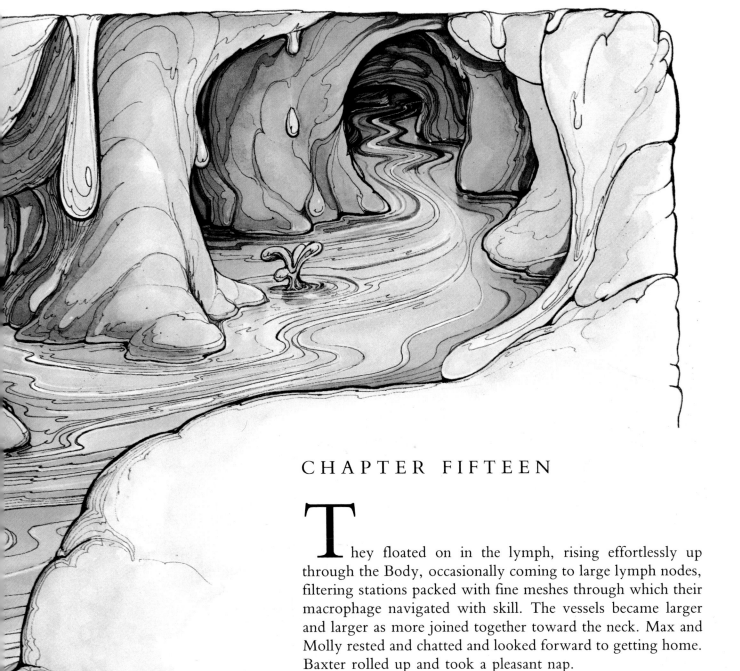

CHAPTER FIFTEEN

They floated on in the lymph, rising effortlessly up through the Body, occasionally coming to large lymph nodes, filtering stations packed with fine meshes through which their macrophage navigated with skill. The vessels became larger and larger as more joined together toward the neck. Max and Molly rested and chatted and looked forward to getting home. Baxter rolled up and took a pleasant nap.

"Here you are," the cell said finally. "You'd better get out here before the opening into the vein." The opening lay dead ahead, so they scrambled off.

"Now up to the skin and out," directed Freewilly.

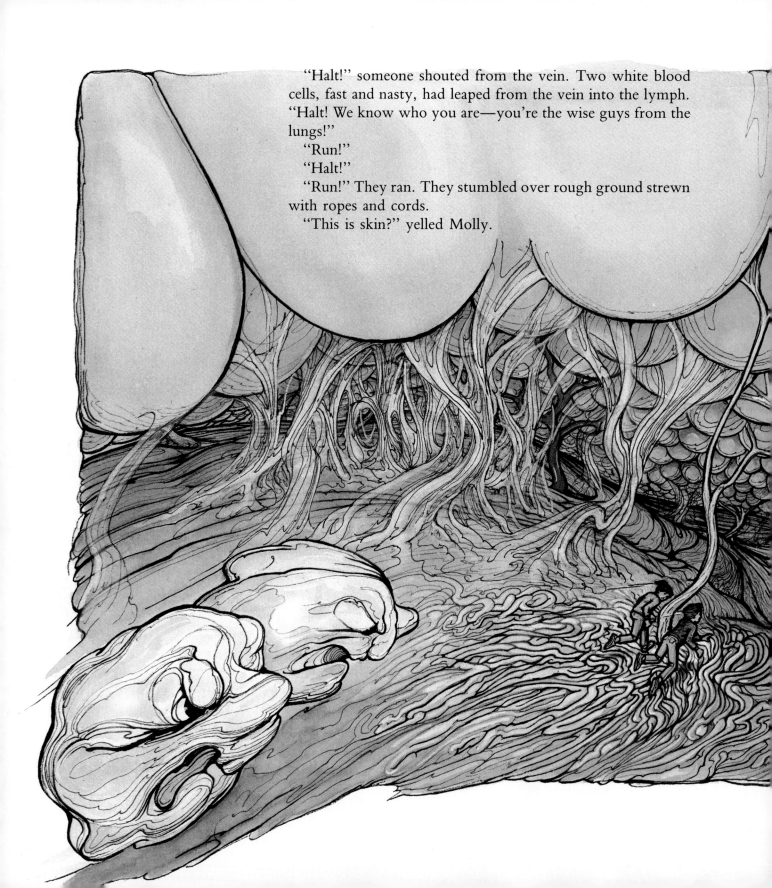

"Halt!" someone shouted from the vein. Two white blood cells, fast and nasty, had leaped from the vein into the lymph. "Halt! We know who you are—you're the wise guys from the lungs!"

"Run!"

"Halt!"

"Run!" They ran. They stumbled over rough ground strewn with ropes and cords.

"This is skin?" yelled Molly.

"The deep skin. Hurry up!" Freewilly urged. Baxter sprang ahead. Max tripped over a coil of hose and Molly nearly crashed into a nerve rising straight up. The two cells pursued them. "Stop in the name of the law!" they yelled.

"Don't stop!" Freewilly yelled, motioning them to a huge, hanging bulb with a tiny opening in its end. They popped into it like rabbits into a hole.

"Gotcha!" yelled the cells and dived for them, crashing into each other with a resounding splat that shook the ground.

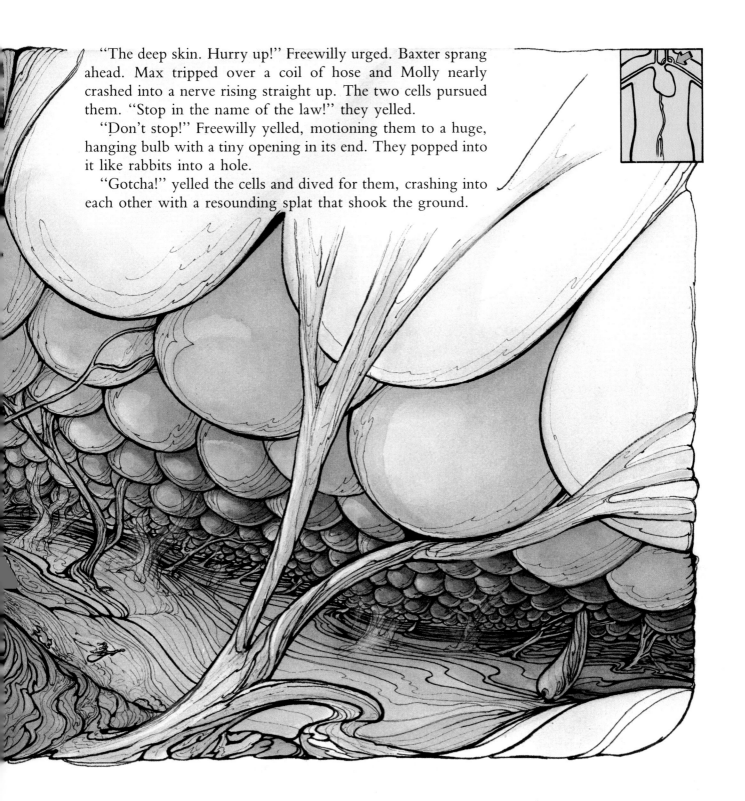

Inside the rabbit hole, Freewilly's voice whispered loudly from above, "Quick, up here, before they come to their senses!" They looked up. A tall, scaly pipe shot straight up out of sight. "A hair," whispered Freewilly. "Climb!" Baxter was already partway up. Max and Molly leaped up, grabbed at the scales, locked their toes in the cracks, and began to hoist themselves up. Freewilly exhorted them to go faster. They climbed desperately until they were nearly exhausted.

"All right," he said at last. "Rest. They can't get you now." Molly clung to the scaly hair and looked down its dizzying shaft, panting for breath. Baxter, relishing the climb, scampered around and around the hair, dashing with enthusiastic sallies after his own tail.

"That was deep skin?" asked Molly.

"Dermis." Freewilly perched above them on the ledge of a scale. "It contains all the blood vessels and nerves of the skin. You may have noticed it's also full of strong fibers, which give the skin its bounce and pull."

"That must have been those ropes I was falling over," said Max.

"I almost ran into a nerve!" said Molly.

"Lots of nerves around here," said Freewilly. "Sensory nerves galore for temperature, touch, pain, pressure—they all hang around the dermis."

"I tripped over a coiled hose, too," said Max.

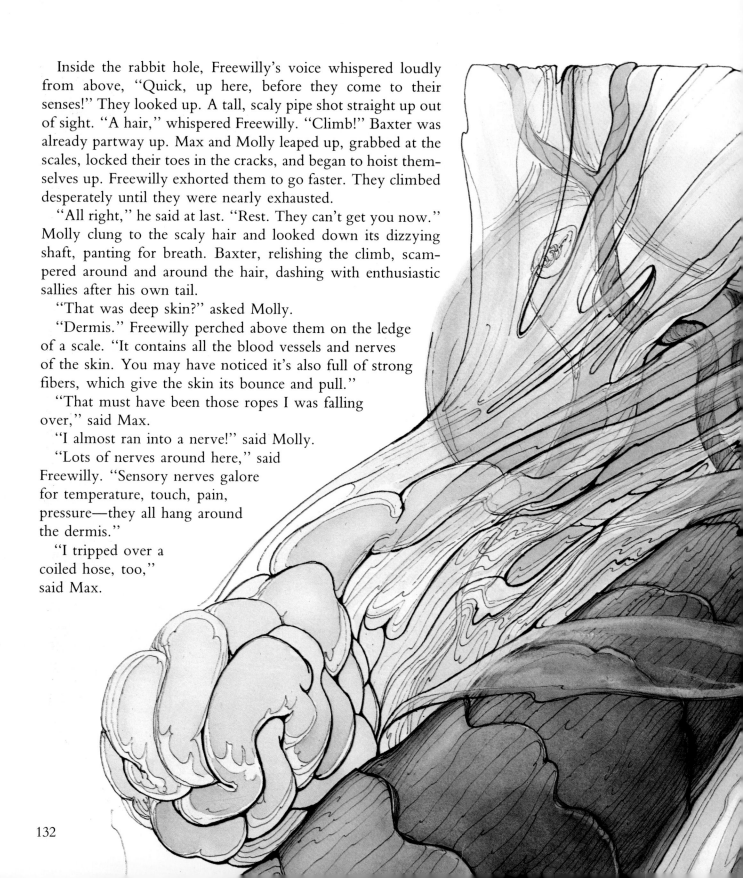

132

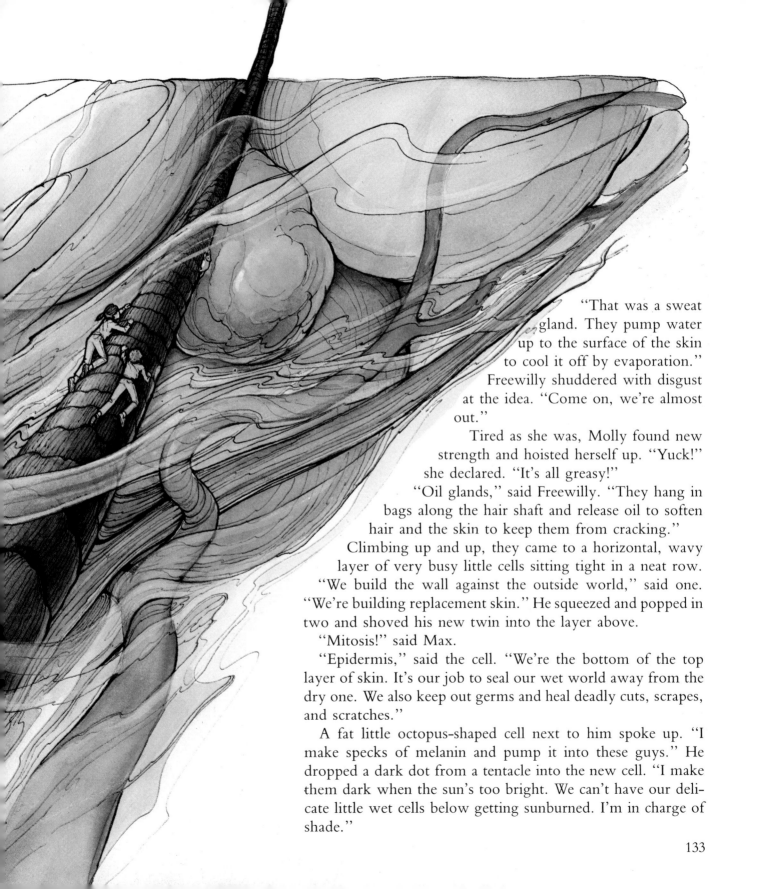

"That was a sweat gland. They pump water up to the surface of the skin to cool it off by evaporation." Freewilly shuddered with disgust at the idea. "Come on, we're almost out."

Tired as she was, Molly found new strength and hoisted herself up. "Yuck!" she declared. "It's all greasy!"

"Oil glands," said Freewilly. "They hang in bags along the hair shaft and release oil to soften hair and the skin to keep them from cracking."

Climbing up and up, they came to a horizontal, wavy layer of very busy little cells sitting tight in a neat row.

"We build the wall against the outside world," said one. "We're building replacement skin." He squeezed and popped in two and shoved his new twin into the layer above.

"Mitosis!" said Max.

"Epidermis," said the cell. "We're the bottom of the top layer of skin. It's our job to seal our wet world away from the dry one. We also keep out germs and heal deadly cuts, scrapes, and scratches."

A fat little octopus-shaped cell next to him spoke up. "I make specks of melanin and pump it into these guys." He dropped a dark dot from a tentacle into the new cell. "I make them dark when the sun's too bright. We can't have our delicate little wet cells below getting sunburned. I'm in charge of shade."

As they climbed higher through the epidermis, the cells became progressively thinner and flatter as they were pushed toward the surface by the rapid growth below. By the time they reached the top, they were flat and dead as cornflakes, and they peeled off and floated away.

"They don't live very long," Molly observed.

"They live on the border of hostile territory," Freewilly replied. "It's dangerous duty. They must produce fresh replacements every day. The world Out There is so treacherous. It keeps scraping and tearing them off, poor things."

Then suddenly, they gasped. They were breathing air!

"We're out!" Max hollered.

"We made it!" yelled Molly. They hauled themselves out of the hole and onto the skin. They jumped and laughed and ran about to kick up cornflakes. Baxter scampered up the hair to watch with cat satisfaction.

"Hurray!" they shouted. When they had calmed down, Max said, "But we're still small." He took out the magnifying glass and unwrapped it.

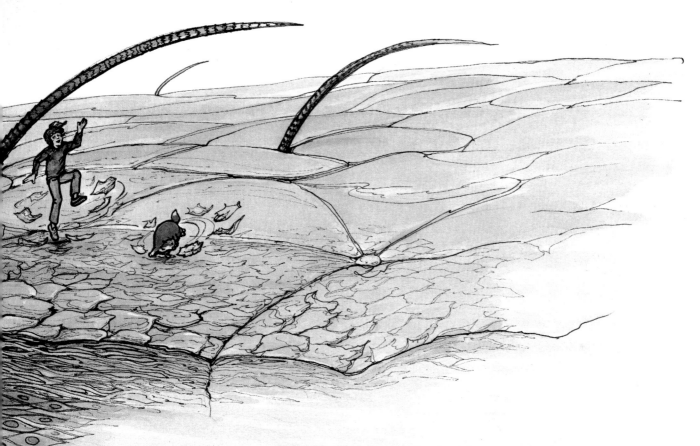

"Speaking of small, where's Freewilly?" said Molly, looking around.

"I haven't seen him."

"I'm sure he came out—OH NO! AIR!!!"

They raced back toward the hair and searched the skin. "Here he is," Max called. Freewilly lay on the dry skin, shriveled, wasted, and still.

"He's dead!" cried Molly. "I never thought!"

"I forgot!" lamented Max. "How stupid!" Molly picked him up and held him tenderly in her hand, and tears rolled down her face.

"Oh no," she wept. "We were so careless, and he saved our lives." A teardrop fell into her hand, meandered across her palm, and bumped into Freewilly. It hesitated, quivered, and merged. He stirred. "He's still alive! I saw him move! Quick, more water."

Max spied a bead of sweat on the opening of a sweat duct. "Here," he shouted. "Dump him in!" Molly dropped him in. He sank.

CHAPTER SIXTEEN

Please, Freewilly," Molly begged. "Don't die! Breathe the water!" Slowly he revived, then he sat bolt upright and took a deep breath.

"Ahhh," he said in a cheery voice. "That was dumb. I should have known what would happen out here. I just got carried away, and the next thing I knew I was flat out on those dry flakes and couldn't even talk."

"You're alive!" cried Molly. "We saved you! We knew what to do and put you in water."

"Well, how about that. Thank you very much." He looked around at the baked desert of the skin and shuddered. "This place is horrible!" He threw up his hands. "And this drop is drying up. I have to go."

"Oh, please stay, we'll keep you wet," said Molly.

"I can't live here any more than you can live in there. That's a lesson I learned the hard way. No, I have to return." He looked up at them and added, "But I must admit you were the best diversion I've had in at least ten thousand years. Now take care of yourselves. I have very important chores to do. I have to go teach all those cells how to get along." With that he sprang up, stretched out thin as an eel, flipped, and made a perfect swan dive down into the sweat duct—and disappeared. Molly waved sadly at the evaporating bead of water.

"Well, that's that," said Max. He sat down, fingering the magnifying glass, and gazed up. Molly looked up. Rafters the size of mountains crossed the attic roof. "We're still tiny," he despaired. "There's no way we can get enough electricity down here to activate this glass. If we walked forever we'd still be in the attic, and the only electricity up here is in that light. We'd have to crawl up the walls and down the cord . . ." Molly sat down in dejected stupor. After a long time, Max said, "We're finished."

"I'm not so sure," said Molly.

"How come?"

"Well, we keep thinking it's electricity that makes the glass work, and that's true. Everytime we got bigger or smaller, we had just gotten zapped. But we've been overlooking one other possibility. It might be the light that goes with electricity. It's so obvious, I never thought of it till now."

Max sprang up. "Maybe that's it!" but then his face fell again. "There's not enough light in here either. It's dim and miles away." He pointed up at the lone bare bulb hanging from the attic roof. "We could try to focus it like the eye does. That would make it brighter in one small spot, and if we're in that spot . . . Just be sure the glass is pointed in the right direction, I don't want to shrink any more."

"Magnify." He held it up to

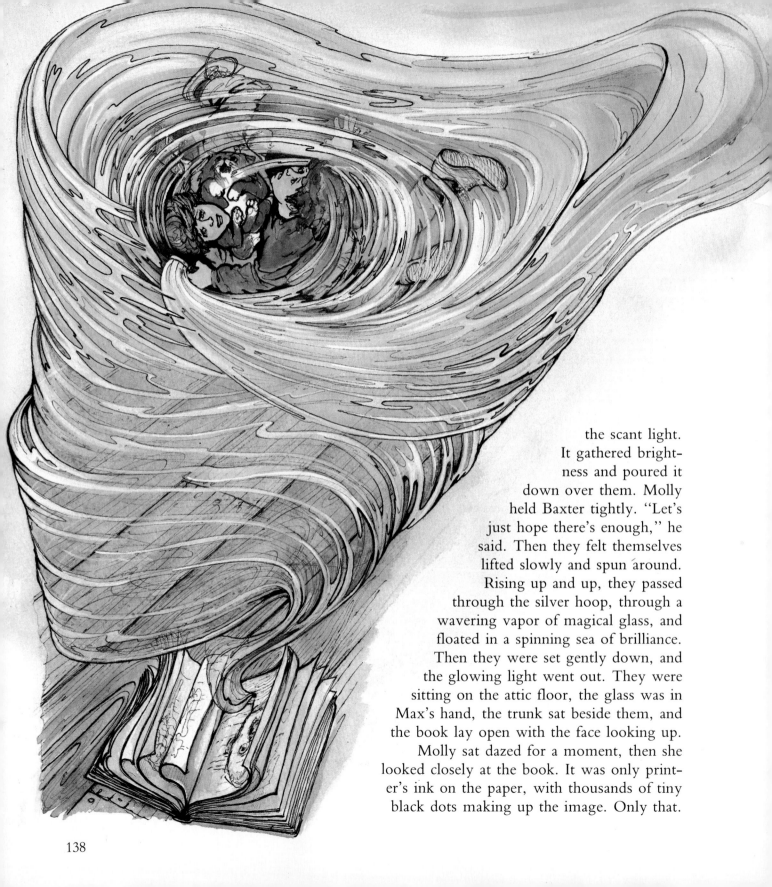

the scant light. It gathered brightness and poured it down over them. Molly held Baxter tightly. "Let's just hope there's enough," he said. Then they felt themselves lifted slowly and spun around. Rising up and up, they passed through the silver hoop, through a wavering vapor of magical glass, and floated in a spinning sea of brilliance. Then they were set gently down, and the glowing light went out. They were sitting on the attic floor, the glass was in Max's hand, the trunk sat beside them, and the book lay open with the face looking up. Molly sat dazed for a moment, then she looked closely at the book. It was only printer's ink on the paper, with thousands of tiny black dots making up the image. Only that.

"Max! Molly!" Grandma called from downstairs, startling them. "That lightning is getting too close. You'd better come down until it's over."

"We've only been gone a few seconds!" exclaimed Max.

"We must have been stuck in time, like you said," said Molly.

"I only meant slower time, but 'stuck' somehow sounds more like it."

"Did it really happen? Look, this is just an ordinary book, and my clothes aren't even wet!"

"I'm not sure," said Max. "Part of me says it couldn't be true, but part of me says it was. But just in case, let's put this glass away before something else happens."

"Okay, I sure wouldn't want to be zapped into a rafter." They quickly replaced the magnifying glass in its case and put it and the old book back into the trunk. Then they shoved the trunk back into the dark corner. Max pulled the light cord, and they went downstairs, leaving the attic to the lonely sound of the rain.

They found Grandma in the kitchen, a frosted cake on the counter, and Baxter curled on his pillow scrubbing his whiskers with placid composure. He looked up and meowed when Molly went over to scratch his head. He rolled his head sideways, closed his eyes, and purred loudly.

"Baxter!" said Molly. "You're wet!"

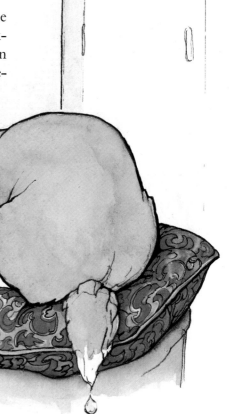

GLOSSARY

abdomen   Lower half of the body between the diaphragm and the pelvis.

absorption   Passage of material into or through cells. Food is absorbed by the small *intestine*.

adrenal glands   *Endocrine* (hormone-secreting) *glands* that lie above the kidneys. The adrenal medulla (the inside layer) produces the *hormone* adrenaline; the adrenal cortex (the outside layer) produces sex hormones and hormones that regulate the kidney.

air sacs (alveoli)   Tiny air spaces in the *lung*. Oxygen and carbon dioxide are exchanged through their walls.

antibodies   Chemicals produced by the immune system to kill bacteria.

aorta   The largest artery. It carries blood from the left *ventricle* of the *heart* to all parts of the body.

artery   A blood vessel carrying blood away from the *heart*.

atrium   The chamber of the *heart* that receives blood from the *veins*. The right atrium receives blood from the body; the left atrium receives blood from the *lungs*.

autonomic nervous system   The division of the *peripheral nervous system* that regulates the body's internal environment, temperature, pressure, oxygen, and food supply. It is divided into the *sympathetic* and the *parasympathetic* systems.

axon   The long extension (tail) of a *neuron* that transmits a nerve impulse to other neurons.

bladder   The stretchy, hollow organ, deep in the *pelvis,* that collects and stores urine from the two *ureters*.

blood   The red fluid that flows through the *circulatory system*. It contains red cells, responsible for oxygen transport, and white cells, the part of the body's defense system that hunts for germs and other invaders. These cells float in plasma, a fluid made up mostly of water that carries food, wastes, and also the platelets, small particles responsible for blood clotting.

bone   The hardest tissue. It supports and protects the body. Hollow long bones contain marrow, where new blood cells are made. The ends of moving bones are coated with smooth, slippery cartilage to decrease friction in joints.

brain   The center of the *central nervous system,* divided into the two cerebral hemispheres, the cerebellum, and the brain stem. Consists of about three pounds of nervous tissue packed into the skull. It is the body's master computer, with 25 billion *neurons,* each connected directly or indirectly to 100,000 other neurons. It is responsible for all senses, thought, and motion.

capillary   The smallest blood vessel. Food, oxygen, and nutrients pass from capillaries to the cells. The smallest *lymphatic* vessels are also called capillaries.

cartilage   Rubbery, smooth, glistening white tissue found in joints, the ear, and the nose.

cell   Tiny living unit. Billions of cells make up the human body. A typical cell consists of *cytoplasm* surrounded by a cell membrane. Important structures of the cytoplasm are the *endoplasmic reticulum, ribosomes, mitochondria, lysosomes,* the *Golgi apparatus,* and the *nucleus.* The nucleus contains the *DNA,* the inherited *genetic code,* which directs each cell function in the body.

central nervous system   The brain and spinal cord.

chromosome   The condensed form taken by the *DNA (genetic code)* in the *nucleus* during *mitosis.* A human cell has 23 pairs of chromosomes.

circulatory system (cardiovascular system) Transport system for the blood, linking all parts of the body. It consists of the *heart,* the *arteries,* the *veins,* the *capillaries,* and the *blood.* It is closely tied to the *lymphatic circulatory system.*

cochlea   The hollow spiral of bone in the inner ear that contains the hearing receptors.

cytoplasm   The jellylike substance inside a cell where chemical activities take place.

dendrite   Projections of a *neuron* that are specialized to receive nerve impulses at *synapses.*

diaphragm   The thin, dome-shaped sheet of muscle that separates the chest from the *abdomen.* In diaphragmatic breathing, the diaphragm contracts (tightens) and flattens. This pulls down the contents of the abdomen, enlarges the chest, and pulls air into the *lungs.* When the diaphragm relaxes, it bulges up and air is expelled.

digestive juices   Products of the salivary glands, *stomach, pancreas,* and *liver* that chemically break down food so that the body can absorb and use it.

digestive system   The group of organs responsible for chewing, swallowing, and digesting food, absorbing food into the *blood,* and disposing of undigested wastes. In the mouth, teeth grind the food, and saliva from the salivary glands begins chemical digestion. The food is then swallowed down the *esophagus* to the *stomach,* small *intestine,* large intestine (colon), rectum, and anus.

DNA (deoxyribonucleic acid)   Long, spiral-ing, double, threadlike molecules found in the cell nucleus. Each molecule makes up one chromosome, which contains many genes. Each gene carries an inherited trait such as eye or hair color.

ear   The organ for hearing. The external ear consists of the pinna (shell), ear canal, and eardrum; the middle ear is the space behind the eardrum that contains the hammer, anvil, and stirrup bones as well as the entrance to the *eustachian tube;* the inner ear consists of the *cochlea* and *semicircular canals.* Sound waves vibrate the eardrum and are transmitted by the bones to a window in the cochlea. Hairlike receptor sensory neurons in the cochlea translate the vibrations into nerve impulses and transmit them to the brain.

endocrine gland   A gland that delivers its product by way of the blood.

endocrine system   A group of *glands*—the pituitary, pineal, thyroid, parathyroid, pancreas (islets of Langerhans), and *adrenal*—that work closely with the nervous system and make chemical messengers, called hormones, for transport by the blood. Hormones signal "target" tissues to perform an activity. Some activities controlled by the endocrine system are growth, use of food by cells (metabolism), salt and water balance, reaction to stress, and reproduction.

endoplasmic reticulum (ER)   Rough ER consists of membranes in the cell to which *ribosomes* attach. Smooth ER (without ribosomes) packages the products of ribosomes for transport out of the cell.

epiglottis   The cartilage trapdoor at the top of the *trachea* (windpipe). It folds down during swallowing to prevent food or liquid from being inhaled into the *lungs.*

esophagus   The soft, muscle-lined tube that carries food from the throat to the stomach.

eustachian tube   The small tube connecting the middle ear with the throat. It allows air pressure to equalize on both sides of the eardrum.

exocrine gland   A gland (salivary, pancreas, liver, sweat) that delivers its product by way of a duct.

eye   The organ of sight. Light passes through the cornea, the clear front of the eye, then through the pupil to the *lens* and on to the *retina*. The retinal sensory receptors, the rods and cones, translate light into nerve impulses and send them to the *brain*.

fallopian tube   One of a pair of hollow tubes that collect an ovum (egg) from the ovary and transport it to the *uterus*.

genetic code   Inherited characteristics carried in genes; sections of the *DNA* molecules in the cell *nucleus*.

germs   Microscopic invading organisms capable of multiplying and causing disease. Bacteria are germs that can cause pneumonia, tetanus, and other infections.

gland   A group of cells that produce and discharge a substance.

Golgi apparatus   A structure of folded *membranes* in a cell that gathers and packages the cell's product for transport out of the cell.

heart   The muscular pump of the circulatory system. It has a left and a right side, each with two chambers: an *atrium* and a *ventricle*. Valves close off the atria from the ventricles: on the right, the tricuspid valve; on the left, the bicuspid, or mitral, valve. The heart relaxes, swells, and fills with blood from a vein (this is called diastole). Then it squeezes and pumps the blood out an artery (this is called systole).

hemoglobin   Molecules in red blood cells that gather or release oxygen and give the cells their characteristic red color.

hormone   A chemical messenger made by an *endocrine gland* and carried in the blood.

immune system (defense department)   The system that protects the body from disease. It includes white blood cells, which search for and destroy germs.

insulin   A hormone produced by the islets of Langerhans, *endocrine* glands in the pancreas. It allows cells to absorb food through their walls.

intestine   The hollow tube beyond the stomach that digests, absorbs, transports, and disposes of food. The small intestine is about nine feet long and $1\frac{1}{2}$ inches in diameter. It leads from the stomach to the large intestine, which is about four feet long but almost three inches in diameter.

ion   An atom or group of atoms that has gained or lost an electron and so acquired an electric charge.

iris   The colored ring of the outside of the *eye*. It controls the amount of light that passes through its opening, the pupil.

joint   Connection between two bones.

joint capsule   Fibrous tissue that encases a moving joint and seals it in oily fluid.

kidney   One of a pair of organs in the *urinary system* that clean the blood of wastes resulting from cellular *metabolism* (respiration) and that regulate the water balance of the body. Each kidney consists of about one million *nephrons*. The urine they produce is drained by collecting tubules into a *ureter*.

lens   The clear, bulging disk behind the *iris*, which controls the fine focusing of light onto the *retina*.

ligaments   Tough, fibrous bands that strap together the ends of bones in a joint.

liver   Large organ, part of the *digestive system*. It stores food and secretes bile, the digestive juice that dissolves fats. Bile is stored in a sac in the gallbladder until it is needed in the small *intestine*. The liver works with the circulatory system by removing toxins (poisons) from the blood as it passes through. White blood cells (Kuppfer cells) in the liver channels kill invading bacteria.

lungs   The main organs of the *respiratory system*. They contain millions of air sacs (alveoli) surrounded by capillaries, where oxygen is exchanged for carbon dioxide in the blood. The *trachea* (windpipe) branches into smaller bronchial tubes, still smaller bronchioles, and finally into air sacs. About 90 gallons of air enter the lungs every hour.

lymphatic circulatory system   Lymph capillaries and vessels collect the fluid that gets squeezed out of the blood capillaries. This fluid, called lymph, bathes the cells. It drains into lymph capillaries and then into larger lymph vessels and finally is carried up to the neck, where it is emptied back into the blood. Lymph nodes along the way filter the lymph and act as part of the *immune system* (defense department).

lysosome   In a cell, a small spherical structure that contains destroying chemicals.

macrophage   A large cell of the *immune system* (defense department). It can create pseudopods (false feet) to engulf its prey.

meiosis   A form of cell division for *reproduction*. It results in cells that contain only half of the *genetic code.*

membrane   A thin flexible film that covers, or surrounds, or divides cells.

metabolism   All the processes, chemical and physical, by which an organism maintains itself and produces energy to live.

mitochondria   Bean-shaped structures within cells. They produce energy by cellular *respiration.* They are the "power plants" of the cell.

mitosis   A form of cell division. The *DNA (genetic code)* duplicates itself, the two sets separate, and the cytoplasm divides, making two identical cells.

muscle   The active tissue of the *musculoskeletal system.* Muscle cells contract to produce movement. Voluntary muscles are striped (striated) and are controlled by the conscious brain. Involuntary muscles are smooth and control unconscious motion, such as *peristalsis.* Cardiac muscles, found only in the heart, are striated and cross-connected, forming meshlike patterns. They are controlled by the *autonomic nervous system,* but specialized muscle cells in the heart can keep it beating without nervous control.

musculoskeletal system   The 650 muscles and 206 bones constituting this system are responsible for supporting the body, protecting its internal organs, and motion. The system allows the body to interact with its environment.

nephron   The working unit of a kidney, consisting of a glomerulus (a filter head containing a blood capillary network), which strains fluids out of the blood, and of tubules that collect and transport it, selecting certain elements and putting them back into the blood. What is left is urine, water, and cellular wastes.

nerve   A bundle of *axons* of the *peripheral nervous system,* each coated with myelin, a fatty sheath that increases the speed at which nerves can signal messages. Myelin insulates nerves and gives them a white appearance.

nervous system   The controller of all body activities, both conscious and unconscious. The *central nervous system* and the *peripheral nervous system* are its two parts.

neuron   A cell of the *nervous system* that receives electrochemical messages on its *dendrites* and cell body and transmits them down its *axon.* This is called depolarization, and it is accomplished by the transport of *ions* through the neuron's cell *membrane.* A depolarized neuron signals another neuron across a gap called a synapse by releasing chemical neurotransmitters. They cross the synaptic gap and land on the receptor sites of the second neuron, triggering its depolarization. Motor neurons transfer orders from the brain or spinal cord to the muscles. Sensory neurons carry messages to the brain from sense organs. Intermediate neurons make up all the complex, computerlike interconnections between neurons.

nucleus   The large sphere in a cell that contains its *DNA (genetic code),* which provides the cell's characteristics and directs its activities.

organ   A group of tissues organized to perform a specific function; for example, the heart, kidney, or liver.

pancreas   A double organ lying behind the stomach. As an *exocrine gland,* it secretes several digestive juices through a duct into the small intestine, which digests proteins, carbohydrates, and fats. As an *endocrine gland,* it also produces the hormone insulin, necessary for cells to absorb food through their walls.

parasympathetic nervous system Division of the *autonomic nervous system* that maintains the normal unconscious running of the internal organs.

pelvis The pitlike space at the bottom of the abdomen containing the bladder, ovaries, uterus, and rectum.

perception The activity of certain areas of the brain that receive messages from the sensory neurons and form impressions, which are then relayed to other areas of the brain to be integrated into the more complex processes of understanding, learning, responding, and thinking.

peripheral nervous system The system of nerves that enter or leave the brain and spinal cord. It is divided into the somatic nervous system, which relates to the outside world, controlling the voluntary muscles and transmitting messages from the sense organs; and the autonomic nervous system, which maintains the body's internal environment.

peristalsis Organized contractions of smooth-muscle cells within the walls of the *esophagus* and *intestine*. It gently squeezes and propels food through the digestive tract. Swallowing is peristalsis.

pituitary gland An endocrine gland attached to and directed by the hypothalamus, the part of the brain controlling unconscious activities. The pituitary is called the master gland because it secretes hormones that orchestrate the activities of other endocrine glands as well as those of many tissues and organs.

proteins Organic compounds that make up the principal components of animal cells.

reproduction The process by which a species perpetuates itself. In humans, it consists of the fertilization of an ovum (egg) by a sperm, resulting eventually in a baby. Ova and sperm, produced by *meiosis,* contain only one-half of the *genetic code* of each parent. United, they will form one cell with the full 46 *chromosomes.*

reproductive system The group of organs responsible for *reproduction.* In the female, the reproductive system consists of the ovaries (which produce ova, or eggs), the *fallopian tubes,* the *uterus,* and the vagina; in the male, the testicles (which produce sperm), the spermatic cord, the prostate gland, and the *urethra.*

respiration This word has two meanings. Cellular respiration is the process by which a cell converts food into energy by using oxygen. Lung respiration is the exchange of oxygen for carbon dioxide between *air sacs* and neighboring *capillaries.*

respiratory system The organs that inhale and exhale air and allow the exchange of oxygen and carbon dioxide between themselves and the blood. The system consists of the nose, mouth, throat, *epiglottis, trachea,* bronchi, bronchioles, *lungs,* and *air sacs.* In breathing, muscles raise the ribs and the diaphragm contracts. These actions increase the effective volume of the chest cavity, causing air to rush into the lungs. The vocal cords are tight bands stretched across the trachea just below the epiglottis. When air rushes out, they can be made to vibrate, creating voice.

retina The inner lining of the *eye,* made up of light-sensitive cells: the rods and cones and their many *neuron* connections. The central point, the fovea, is the area of clearest color vision. The outer areas are more receptive in dim light.

ribosomes The worker elements within a *cell.* They read messages from the *nucleus* and manufacture the cell's product.

saline Water containing a small amount of salt. It is the basic fluid of the body.

saliva Liquid product of the salivary glands. It moistens food and contains some digestive juices. Starch is converted into sugar in the mouth by saliva.

sanitary Germ-free, clean.

semicircular canals Sense organs of balance and motion in the inner ear.

sense organs These organs translate and transmit information from the external environment to the brain. The eye, ear, nose, tongue, and skin are special sense organs.

skeleton   The total structure of all 206 bones in the body.

skin   The organ that separates the body from its environment. The deep layer, the dermis, contains blood vessels, sensory nerve endings, hair follicles, and sweat and oil glands. The top layer, the epidermis, seals the body from the outside environment. The skin regulates heat and water loss. It protects the body's deep tissues, and it senses touch, heat, pressure, and pain.

spinal column (backbone)   The flexible shaft of vertebral bones *(vertebrae)* that forms the central supporting pillar of the skeleton. It also surrounds and protects the spinal cord.

spinal cord   The long extension of the *brain* encased in the *spinal column*.

stomach   The hollow, muscular organ of the digestive tract that lies below the heart. Cells in its lining secrete strong acid to digest food. It stores and grinds about a quart of food at a time.

sympathetic nervous system   The division of the *autonomic nervous system* that takes over in stressful situations (red alert).

synapse   The junction between two *neurons*. The point of transfer of a message from one neuron to another. Chemical neurotransmitters jump the gap to trigger the second neuron.

system   A group of organs that function together: the *musculoskeletal system,* the *digestive system,* the *respiratory system,* the *urinary system,* the *nervous system,* the *endocrine system,* and the *reproductive system.*

teeth   Enameled, bonelike structures in the mouth that bite and grind food. A human has two sets. The 20 baby (deciduous) teeth are replaced eventually by 32 permanent teeth. Their enamel is the hardest substance in the body.

tendon   A dense, strong fiber that attaches a muscle to a bone across a joint.

tissue   A group of similar specialized cells that work together to perform a function: for example, muscle tissue.

tonsils   Masses of lymphatic tissue that act as part of the body's defense system, guarding against bacteria in the air and food.

trachea (windpipe)   A flexible tube made of cartilage rings that carries air to and from the *lungs.* At the top end are the *epiglottis* and vocal cords.

ureter   A tube that transports urine from the *kidney* to the *bladder.*

urethra   The duct that carries urine in the female, urine or sperm in the male, from the *bladder* to outside the body.

uterus   A muscular organ about the size and shape of a pear deep in the female *pelvis.* It is part of the female *reproductive system* and is specially lined with tissues that can imbed and nurture a fertilized cell. It grows larger as the cell develops into a baby. In the labor of childbirth, it squeezes and pushes the baby down the vagina. The remaining imbedding tissue, now a placenta, is expelled and the uterus shrinks to near-normal size.

urinary system   Consists of the *kidneys, ureters, bladder,* and *urethra.* It regulates salt, water, and mineral levels in the body and removes cellular wastes resulting from *metabolism,* creating urine.

valve   A structure of flaps in the *heart* and some *veins* that permits *blood* to flow in only one direction. Valves open and close with each heartbeat.

vein   A blood vessel carrying blood toward the *heart.*

vena cava   Either of two great veins, the superior vena cava or inferior vena cava, that carry blood into the right *atrium.*

ventricle   One of the two pumping chambers of the *heart.* The right ventricle pumps blood to the *lungs* to be oxygenated; the left ventricle pumps oxygenated blood to all the body cells.

vertebra   One of the bones of the spine. There are seven in the neck (cervical), twelve in the chest (thoracic), and five in the abdomen (lumbar). Each is cushioned from the ones above and below by *cartilage* disks.

ACKNOWLEDGEMENTS

Many people encouraged and contributed to this book. I would like to acknowledge the staff of W. H. Freeman and Company, especially my editor, Karen McDermott, for her tireless efforts and Patrick Cunningham, art director, for his ingenious design.

I want also to thank Ronald Feinstein, who offered much valuable advice as an educational consultant, and Matthew Holt, who lent his handsome face to Max and Molly.

The Magic Anatomy Book

Composed by York Graphic Services
in Bembo using the Linotron 202 system
Printed by Kingsport Press
on 60 lb. Patina Matte
Bound by Kingsport Press
in Joanna Devon cloth
with Multicolor Aztec Blue endsheets